ANTOINE LAVOISIER

and the Revolution in Chemistry

ANTOINE LAVOISIER

and the Revolution in Chemistry

———— ❧ ————

REBECCA B. MARCUS

FRANKLIN WATTS, INC.
575 Lexington Avenue, New York 22

FIRST PRINTING
Library of Congress Catalog Card Number 64-11918
© Copyright 1964 by Franklin Watts, Inc.
Printed in the United States of America
by The Moffa Press, Inc.

ACKNOWLEDGMENTS

My thanks to Denis I. Duveen, Fellow of the Royal Institute of Chemistry of Great Britain and North Ireland, for his great generosity in making available to me material from his superb collection of Lavoisier documents, engravings, and other papers. As I listened to Mr. Duveen speak to me of Antoine Lavoisier, his own enthusiasm for the work of the great French chemist became contagious, and Lavoisier himself seemed to come alive before my eyes. I hope I have been able to carry some of this enthusiasm over to those who read this book.

And, my very special thanks to Mr. Duveen for his critical reading of the manuscript before the book was published.

Additional thanks to Dr. William A. Smeaton of University College, London, for making clearer to me the relationship between Lavoisier and other chemists at the time of the French Revolution.

REBECCA B. MARCUS

CONTENTS

ANTOINE LAVOISIER

and the Revolution in Chemistry

PROLOGUE

᷿ TOWARD THE END of the eighteenth century two great revolutions occurred in Europe. One, the French Revolution, started on July 14, 1789 with the storming of the Bastille in Paris. Although it took a number of years for the excesses and terrors of this bloody revolt against the French monarchy and nobility to cease, in the end the people of France achieved freedom from tyranny.

The other, the revolution in chemistry, also started in France with the publication in 1783 of a scientific paper called *Reflections on Phlogiston*, by Antoine-Laurent Lavoisier. This revolution continued to gain support upon the publication in 1787 of a book called *Method of Chemical Nomenclature* by four French chemists—Guyton deMorveau, Berthollet, Fourcroy, and the same Lavoisier. Finally it reached its climax in 1789 with the appearance of Antoine-Laurent Lavoisier's *Traité Élémentaire de Chime*. The effects of this second, "chemical revolution" were widespread. Indeed, it is responsible for having placed our present study of chemistry on an orderly, rational, scientific basis.

Antoine-Laurent Lavoisier was destined to play a part in both of these revolutions. He was the prime mover— we might rightly say the "brains"—of the revolution in chemistry. But of the other, the political revolution, he was a tragic victim.

Let us start from the beginning.

A FAMILY OF LAWYERS

THEIR FIRST CHILD had just been born to Jean-Antoine Lavoisier and his wife Émilie on that warm day of August 26, 1743. Because the child was a boy, the parents carried on the two-hundred-year-old family tradition of naming the oldest son Antoine. In their comfortable, spacious room of his large house in Paris the young father sat at his wife's bedside talking quietly to her about the plans for the baby's baptism the next day. She agreed to have the name Laurent added as a middle name after the child's great-uncle Father Laurent Waroquier, and to ask the uncle to act as godfather.

There was another tradition in the families of each of the young parents. In the last few generations both families had produced distinguished members of the legal profession. Although they had originally been farmers in the village of Villers-Cotterets about fifty miles north of Paris

—where they still owned some property—the Lavoisiers had left the farm many years before. Jean-Antoine's father was a prosperous lawyer, as was the young man himself; his maternal grandfather and uncle were well-established lawyers, too. From this uncle, Jean-Antoine had inherited a large sum of money, the house he now lived in, and his place as attorney to the chief judiciary court of Paris. What could have been more natural for the young man of such a family than to marry Émilie Punctis, daughter of a lawyer who was secretary to the vice-admiral of France? And now, here was a new Antoine Lavoisier who, his parents hoped, would in time take his place alongside his father in the legal profession.

The house in which Antoine's parents lived was a mansion set back in a garden on a quiet, fashionable side-street on the right bank of the Seine. It was not far from the river and the Tuilleries gardens. The many glass windows in the Lavoisier home gave evidence of the prosperity of the owner, since the tax on glass was so heavy that only the wealthy could afford it. As he grew, little Antoine-Laurent did not lack for sunshine and brightness in his home, nor space in which to run and play.

When Antoine was two years old a sister, Marie-Émilie, was born. She was a pretty child and when she became old enough loved to share in her brother's play. Accompanied by a nurse or by their mother, the two children sometimes went to the Tuilleries gardens to play with other children of well-to-do Parisians. Often they went to the nearby Seine to watch the boats carrying cargoes to and from the ports near Paris. In warm weather they were taken for drives in an open carriage through the parks and gardens of the city, past palaces and great city mansions of the king and the nobility.

At the time of these outings, the Lavoisier children were too young to give much thought to the dirty, foul-smelling streets with their gutters of filthy sewage. Sometimes they had to trail behind a slow-moving cart that was carrying barrels of water to private homes, for there was no overall plan of water supply for the city of Paris. Often, too, the streets were blocked by herds of cattle being driven to one of the slaughter houses in the city. But when at last the children reached the beautiful parks and woods they breathed deeply of the clean, earthy air and quickly forgot the squalor of the streets through which they had passed. And on their return home, there was their gay, smiling mother to greet them.

Then, in the year 1748, tragedy struck the happy Lavoisier family. Émilie Punctis Lavoisier, the young wife and mother, died after a short illness and the two little children were left motherless.

When the grief-stricken Jean-Antoine Lavoisier returned home after his wife's funeral, he knew he would have to be both father and mother to his two children. But before too many weeks had passed, he clearly saw that they needed the special kind of tenderness and care that only a woman who loved them could give the children. It was fortunate indeed that there were two such women—their grandmother Mme. Punctis and their aunt Mlle. Constance Punctis, who lived just a few streets away. Since she had been widowed recently, Mme. Punctis was sad and lonely in the house she felt was too big for herself and her daughter Constance. She hoped the presence of her son-in-law and her two grandchildren would help ease the sorrow caused by the loss of her husband and her daughter Émilie.

And so Jean-Antoine gave up his house and went with

his children to make his home with Mme. and Mlle. Punctis. Both grandmother and aunt doted on little Marie-Émilie and Antoine-Laurent. Twenty-two-year-old Constance especially became attached to her niece and nephew. It was she who now took the children on their walks and drives to the parks and gardens of Paris, sought suitable playmates for them, and taught them manners and conduct proper for children of two such respected families.

The children spent their summers in Villers-Cotterets, in the country home of Grandmother Lavoisier, where they were free from the restraints of city living. Then, with the arrival of autumn, back they went to the house in the rue de Four-Saint-Eustache to Grandmother Punctis and Aunt Constance.

For a few years Antoine-Laurent learned all his lessons at home. He was a serious child, imaginative, gentle, and lovable, and a good student. But an important part of his education did not come from books. Sometimes his father permitted him to stay up past his bedtime if there were guests from whose conversation the child might profit, for Jean-Antoine wanted his son to become familiar with the men who were among the most important lawyers in Paris. There were times, too, when writers, scientists, artists, and musicians were guests in the house at rue de Four-Saint-Eustache, and these young Antoine-Laurent often met as well. Doubtless the impressions these people left upon him remained with him all of his life.

When Antoine was eleven his father decided the boy should go to school instead of being tutored at home—and of course he must go to the best school in Paris. There, just across the river, was the hundred-year-old Collège Mazarin, the finest and most expensive school in the city, which Jean-Antoine himself had attended. Sons of both the wealthy and the nobility from many parts of France attended this school, some as boarding students, some as day students. For young Antoine, it would be a short walk to the school, and so in 1754, Antoine-Laurent Lavoisier was enrolled at the Collège Mazarin as a day student.

LAVOISIER'S FIRST INTRODUCTION TO
SCIENCE

TWO

✵ SIX DAYS A WEEK Antoine-Laurent walked from his home in the rue de Four-Saint-Eustache to the Collège Mazarin. His way took him through narrow streets to the Pont Neuf which crossed the Seine at the tip of the island on which stood the Cathedral of Notre Dame. From there he walked on to the left bank and the school. Coming back in winter when days were short he hurried through the dark, badly-lit streets that led from the bridge to the bright warmth of home.

The Collège Mazarin rightly deserved its reputation as the best school in Paris, for it counted among its teachers some of the finest scholars in the city. In addition to the usual history, literature, composition, and mathematics, a good deal of time was spent in the study of what was then called natural science. This included astronomy, geology, chemistry, and botany. And in the teaching of these subjects the staff of the school excelled.

The instructor in mathematics and astronomy was Abbé Nicolas Louis de Lacaille, head of the group of mathematicians who had succeeded in calculating the circumference of the earth. At the Collège Mazarin Lacaille had set up a small astronomical observatory which could be used by the students in their study of the heavens. Jean-Étienne Guettard, a well-known geologist and friend of the Lavoisier and Punctis families, taught mineralogy and geology.

The pupils were also instructed in the Linnaean system of botany recently introduced to the scientific world by the Swedish scientist Carl von Linné, better known by his Latinized name of Linnaeus. The instructor who taught the subject was the famous botanist Bernard de Jussieu, then under appointment to the king of France to study and classify the plants in the royal gardens. Not the least among the school's staff was the king's own physician, Professor Bourdelin, who lectured to the students on chemistry. But most popular was the demonstrator in chemistry, Guillaume François Rouelle.

Because the chemistry lectures were so well attended, they were held in the theater of the Jardin du Roi. This was necessary in order to accommodate the many scientists and writers, as well as the fashionable ladies and gentlemen, who joined the students for the lectures. Many came not only to hear Professor Bourdelin's dull lengthy talk, but to watch Rouelle perform his demonstrations. As was customary at that time, when the professor finished his presentation of the topic, he turned the platform over to his demonstrator-assistant.

This was the moment for which the audience waited. Rouelle not only presented his facts in a very clear and interesting way, but by his whole manner delighted his listeners. As one of them wrote: "He usually arrived at the lecture room elegantly attired in a velvet coat, wearing a well-powdered wig, and with a little hat under his arm. Calm enough at the beginning of the lesson, he gradually warmed up to it. If a train of thought became too obscure, he was impatient; he would put his hat on a piece of apparatus, take off his wig, take off his cravat, then, talking all the time, he would unbutton his coat and waistcoat and discard them one after the other. After his ideas became clear, he was animated, he let himself go, and, trusting to his inspiration and his illuminating experiments, entranced his audience."

Sometimes during his demonstrations, if a piece of apparatus was missing, he left the room in search of it without interrupting his talk. He would continue talking, often finishing his speech in the adjoining room. On his return to the lecture hall he would, at the request of the audience, good-naturedly repeat the whole lecture.

Rouelle's lectures and demonstrations made a deep impression on young Lavoisier. The chemistry teacher's clear thinking and logical explanations caught the imagination of the growing boy. There were times, too, when Antoine was permitted to work with Rouelle in his laboratory. From all of this the boy was learning one of the great lessons in the study of science. He was learning that a scientific truth must be reached by experimentation and must be based on proven facts, not on words alone. It was a lesson Lavoisier never forgot.

While Antoine still expected to enter the School of Law

when he should leave the Collège Mazarin, the whole field of science had meanwhile aroused his intense interest. Realizing this, Bernard de Jussieu occasionally took the boy along with him to the gardens at Versailles to assist in identifying plants and in arranging them according to Linnaeus' new system. But even better were the trips he was invited to take with his professor of geology, Dr. Guettard. On these trips they studied the soil and rocks near Paris in order to prepare a geological map of the area. Usually short-tempered and impatient, Professor Guettard nevertheless loved to be with young students, and treated them tolerantly and kindly. Patiently, he taught Antoine to recognize different rocks, minerals, and soils, knowledge which was of no apparent use to an aspiring lawyer.

In all these years as a student, Antoine was also gaining other skills which would be of greater use to him in the family profession. He was learning to organize his ideas both in speaking and in writing, a necessary skill for any capable lawyer. In his desire to excel in everything he undertook, young Lavoisier worked tirelessly at improving his composition and rhetoric. Since he was naturally very bright and quick in learning, these efforts bore fruit, and he was awarded prizes in literature, composition, and public speaking.

By the time Antoine had spent six years at the Collège Mazarin, he had grown from a shy boy to a still-shy but earnest, well-spoken, slender youth of seventeen. He would soon be ready to graduate and to go on to further study. But before graduation, his family was once more visited by a great sorrow. Marie-Émilie, his only sister, died when she was fifteen years old.

The love and devotion that had been shared by the two

children now became centered on Antoine. Aunt Constance, who had been refusing all offers of marriage, became even more attached to her promising nephew. A highly unselfish person, Constance's own personal life took second place to that of the seventeen-year-old youth. Nor did the elder Lavoisier, who had remained a widower these twelve years, care to remarry. Instead he found great comfort and pleasure in the companionship of his young son. The two were to remain close friends for all of Jean-Antoine's life.

THE CONFLICT BETWEEN LAW
AND SCIENCE

❧ In 1761, Antoine-Laurent Lavoisier left the Collège Mazarin to enter the School of Law. It is doubtful that he enrolled in this school because he was dedicated to the idea of following in the profession of his family. Very likely he wanted to please his father, and did not wish to hurt him further so soon after the loss of young Marie-Émilie.

Yet Antoine could not seem to forget the scientific subjects that had so captivated his interest. While he attended his prescribed classes dutifully, he began to limit his social life in order to find time to pursue this other interest. Often he pretended to be ill so that he might be excused from attending dinners and parties, for these took him away from his scientific books, magazines, and experiments. Even these pretenses, however, did not give him

enough free hours for all the scientific ideas he wanted
to explore. Indeed, he even begrudged the time spent
having meals with the family and sought ways to avoid
this encroachment on his day. To this end Antoine put
himself on a diet of milk, which he could drink in his own
room while he worked.

After a few months of this limited diet, friends of the
nineteen-year-old Lavoisier became alarmed and protested
to him that he was ruining his health. One of these sent
him a bowl of cereal with a letter which said, "My dear
Mathematician, you are like all men of letters in whom
the mind is of more value than the body. I beseech you to
arrange your studies on the basis that an additional year on
earth is of more value to you yourself now than a hundred
years in the memory of man."

Perhaps it was this very letter that induced young
Lavoisier to abandon his peculiar diet, although he continued to work away at both his law studies and his science.

During these last two years, Antoine had become especially interested in studying air pressure and its relation
to the weather at different seasons, times, and places. To
investigate this further, he set up a barometer in his home
and kept a record of the air pressure several times a day.
When he was not home, Aunt Constance or one of his
other relatives obliged him by noting the barometer reading. Wherever he went outside Paris he made a record
of the barometric pressure, which he then used to make
comparisons with the air pressure and weather in the city.
Actually all of this amounted to more than just idle curiosity, for the germ of an idea was beginning to grow in his
mind about weather forecasting. However, because he
knew that he needed much more information before he

dared formulate a theory, Antoine, with the help of his friends and relatives, patiently continued to record barometer readings in his journal for most of his life.

Summers and holidays the young man still spent at the Lavoisier family estate in Villers-Cotterets. There, notebook in hand, he wandered in the fields and woods carefully examining and classifying plants, identifying rocks and minerals, and searching for fossils. Nor had Antoine, since his graduation from the Collège Mazarin in 1761, lost touch with his geology teacher, Professor Guettard. The two still took trips around Paris to study the rocks of the region for the geological map of France that Guettard planned to make. In fact, the professor was beginning to look upon Antoine as quite an able junior assistant. Because of the faith he had in young Lavoisier's ability, the geologist in 1763 invited his one-time student to serve as his official assistant in collecting data for this map. Since Antoine was in his third and last year at the School of Law, he accepted the invitation with the provision that he "geologize" only in his spare time.

Thus, in the days left free by his law studies, Lavoisier gathered information for Professor Guettard's geological map of France. Of necessity, most of this research was conducted in the countryside near Paris. Even so, the senior geologist thought his assistant's work valuable enough to have him continue it for three more years. Despite his "geologizing", however, Lavoisier never forgot to record his barometer readings daily, for it had become as much a habit as putting on his shoes in the morning.

It seemed strange that a young man of twenty should care more for work than for the normal activities of other young people his age. Yet so absorbed had he become in both the law and science, that he had time for little else. Then, late in the year of 1763, he graduated from the School of Law. To complete his training, Lavoisier spent the next year in his father's law office preparing for his formal admission to the profession. At last, in 1764, when he was twenty-one, Antoine-Laurent Lavoisier became a licensed lawyer.

But in spite of his new professional standing, Lavoisier's heart was more in his scientific work than in the law. True, he had not been formally trained as a scientist, but then there was not much training to be had in science in the middle of the eighteenth century. Actually, he was as ready as anyone could be at that time to start a scientific career. Still, he did not want to disappoint his father by leaving the traditional family profession before he had given himself a fair chance at practicing it. And so young Lavoisier went to work as a lawyer—but in his free time continued as assistant to Professor Guettard.

While doing some research connected with the geology of the Paris area, Lavoisier had become familiar with several different varieties of the mineral gypsum. When heated, this mineral crumbles to a powder; then, if the powder is mixed with water, it forms a paste which within a few minutes hardens to a solid state. This plaster was called—as it is to this day—plaster of Paris. It is particularly useful because upon hardening it takes the shape of the vessel in which it is poured, and thus can be used to make molds or casts.

Lavoisier became curious about the cause of this behavior of gypsum and began to experiment with it. Using a chemical balance, he found that when heated, gypsum—which is calcium sulphate plus water of crystallization—

loses its water; when mixed again with water, the powder recrystallizes and solidifies.

When he had finished these experiments, Lavoisier was ready to take his first step in the world of chemistry, based on research which he himself had done. One evening, after he had finished work at the law office, he sat down in his room to start writing a paper which he hoped to submit to the Royal Academy of Science. In it he told of his experiments with gypsum and plaster of Paris, and gave his conclusions about the behavior of the mineral.

Lavoisier submitted his paper to the Royal Academy of Science in 1765. Although he was not a member of the Academy, his report was accepted and read before that body. Three years later it was published. Meanwhile, it served to bring the young lawyer to the attention of a group of scientists who were among the most famous in France.

Hardly had Lavoisier submitted his paper when he embarked on another project which carried him still farther from his legal profession and nearer a scientific career. The Royal Academy of Science had just announced that it would offer a prize for an essay describing the best plan for lighting the streets of a big city brightly and economically. Lavoisier intended to enter into the competition for the prize.

To present such a plan, it became necessary to experiment with different kinds of materials to find out which gave the most light at the lowest cost. One story has it that in the course of these experiments Lavoisier lived and worked for six weeks in a darkened room whose windows were covered with black curtains. He wanted his eyes to become accustomed to very small differences in light intensity since he had no exact means of measuring it. Whether or not this is actually true, Lavoisier nevertheless pursued his researches with such care and diligence that the essay he finally wrote was excellent. Although it did not win him the prize of two thousand livres, it did receive special mention. In addition, the king of France, upon the Academy's recommendation, awarded Lavoisier a gold medal for his essay. He received the medal from the hands of the President of the Royal Academy of Science at a large public assembly on April 9, 1766, when he was only twenty-two years old.

Needless to say, Antoine Lavoisier's family felt honored at the recognition the young man had just earned. But they were grieved that Grandmother Punctis had not lived to see it, for she had died earlier that year. As for Jean-Antoine, his pleasure at his son's success was mixed with feelings of another sort. It was becoming more and more obvious to him that Antoine, try as he would, was not cut out to be a lawyer. Only when he was concerned with scientific matters did his son seem truly happy.

To the elder Lavoisier his son's happiness was more important than his own ambitions for him. And, if Antoine were to devote so much of his time and talent to science, he should have the means to equip a laboratory with the finest apparatus obtainable. Fortunately, Antoine had inherited enough money for this from his mother, but could not touch it until he was twenty-five years old. His father therefore took legal steps to enable the young man to receive his inheritance earlier. As a result, at twenty-three Antoine had enough money of his own to free him from financial worries.

Even so, Lavoisier's final break with the legal profession had not yet been made. He still could not quite make up his mind to devote himself entirely to science. After completion of his essay on street lighting the young lawyer-scientist had resumed his geological work. Only a little extra inducement was needed to bring the whole matter to a climax. This inducement was unwittingly supplied by the geologist Jean-Étienne Guettard in the spring of 1767.

TRAVELS WITH GUETTARD

❧ EARLY IN 1767 King Louis had been convinced of the importance of making a geological study of the newly-acquired northeastern provinces of Alsace and Lorraine. One of the reasons given was that he needed a complete picture of the mineral wealth of all of France. Professor Guettard, who was working on his ambitious geological atlas of the country, was of course the logical man to be appointed to undertake this special study.

Guettard agreed to complete this research on the geology of the two new provinces before winter set in. But he knew that by himself he could not finish the work in one summer. He needed an assistant capable enough to be considered a collaborator and agreeable enough to make a four-month trip with him a pleasant one. The son of his friend Jean-Antoine Lavoisier would be ideal for this purpose if he could get the young man and his family to agree to such a trip.

Guettard therefore approached his former pupil with the invitation to join him in June on his geological tour of northeast France. Lavoisier's father gave his consent reluctantly, for he still harbored a faint hope that Antoine would return to law practice. As for Aunt Constance, she gave voice to her worries and fears for Antoine's health and welfare, and to the discomforts and dangers of travel. She also added that the elderly geologist might very likely prove a dull companion for a young man of twenty-four. However, none of her gloomy forebodings prevented Antoine from accepting Guettard's invitation. To placate Aunt Constance, he agreed to let her servant Joseph accompany them, and to write home every day if possible.

Thus, on the afternoon of June 14, 1767, Professor Guettard, Antoine Lavoisier, and Joseph set out from Paris on horseback for the Vosges Mountains in northeastern France. Yet even in the excitement of leaving, Lavoisier took a last barometer reading, and reminded his aunt of her promise to see to it that a record was kept while he was away.

In addition to their personal baggage, barometers, and other instruments, the two geologists took with them a box of chemicals to test soil and rocks. It was also advisable for all three travelers to carry firearms as protection against bandits that frequented the roads. Even with this possibility of danger, however, Lavoisier felt light-hearted as he rode out of the gate of Paris toward the east.

True to his word, Antoine wrote a letter home that first night saying that all was well. Before retiring, too, as he was to do every night, Lavoisier made careful, detailed entries in his journal of the day's doings and of his expenses. At the end of the trip, this journal would serve as a very complete record of all that had been achieved in the four months they were away from Paris.

By the end of the second week, the party arrived in the town of Bourbonne-les-Bains, where both Guettard and the Lavoisier family had friends with whom they were invited to stay. It was a welcome change from the inns where they had spent so many nights. There mail awaited him. Aunt Constance's letters told of all that went on at home. She gave a description of the men who were repairing the stables, and of the kittens the cat had just had. She wrote of the card games she and his father played, and said they were dull because neither Antoine nor Dr. Guettard were present to enliven them. A flood of homesickness swept over Antoine.

Nevertheless, Lavoisier was determined to complete the tour, for he had, in these few weeks, already seen and learned many interesting things. He had visited museums and factories, talked with masons on the method of mixing plaster, examined the drinking water of many towns, and studied the nature of the soil and rocks. Ahead, he knew, would lie visits to mines, climbs in the Vosges Mountains, a side-trip into Switzerland, and a view of the Rhine River at France's border.

Since he was still not very far away from Paris, Lavoisier's aunt and father were not too much worried about him. But as the tour took the party farther from what Mlle. Punctis might have called "civilization", that lady's fears multiplied. Once she wrote, "Take care of yourself for a father and an aunt who live only for you. A letter scarcely reaches us but we are already waiting for the next."

The three men traveled on, sometimes finding comfortable lodgings, sometimes sleeping wherever they could.

One night the only shelter they were able to get was in a drafty loft which smelled of drying onions, with nothing but two dirty mattresses for bedding. In fact, the travelers had to scour the village to find even these meager accommodations. For the first time in his life Lavoisier became acutely aware of the extreme squalor and primitiveness of so many of the French villages. True, he had often heard in Paris that there was much poverty among the people of France, but it was not until he saw it with his own eyes that he actually believed it. Now it was brought home to him forcibly—and gave him much to think about in later years.

The geologists expected to be back at Bourbonne-les-Bains early in October, where once more they would stay with family friends. Lavoisier wrote his father and it was agreed that he would join them there.

Father and son met on October 7. When the geologists left Bourbonne-les-Bains a few days later, Jean-Antoine rode along with them until the road branched off to Villers-Cotterets, where Jean-Antoine was expected at the family estate. Antoine and Professor Guettard, with Joseph in the rear, continued on their way to Paris, arriving on October 19, four months after they had left. But Antoine remained in the city only two days, then left for Villers-Cotterets for a few weeks of long-needed rest.

Upon his return to Paris in November, Lavoisier began to compile the notes he had taken for the geological atlas of France. And, more important, he became aware that he was being mentioned with great respect in scientific circles for the research he had done with Guettard.

At that point, the die was cast. Antoine-Laurent Lavoisier finally abandoned the traditional profession of his family for the life of a scientist.

THE SCIENCE OF CHEMISTRY TO
LAVOISIER'S TIME

FIVE

❧ ALTHOUGH LAVOISIER's tour with Professor Guettard was mainly geological in nature, the trip necessarily involved some work in chemistry. It was toward this branch of science that the young Frenchman's interest gravitated. Indeed, the impressions previously made on the boy by Dr. Rouelle, the demonstrator in chemistry, had carried over to the grown man. These, in addition to Antoine's successes in his experiments with gypsum and in street lighting, doubtless helped Lavoisier to choose chemistry as the branch of science in which he wished to work.

At this time, however, the field of chemistry was limited in scope. In fact, not until the work of Robert Boyle about a hundred years earlier had chemistry even begun to be called a science. If we were to accept as a definition of a science "knowledge gained and verified by exact observation, methodically formulated and arranged in a rational system" we could just barely stretch that definition to include the chemistry of Boyle's day. True, a good deal was known about chemicals, but little of this information was arranged and classified in a truly scientific fashion.

Chemistry earned the right to be called a science only after having gone through a number of stages. The first stage was tied up with the life of early man who unwittingly used chemistry in so simple a matter as making a fire. He knew that some materials would burn and that others would not; some would burn more readily, others took a long time to kindle. And he also knew that any fire would burn better if it were fanned or had air blown on it. In addition, ancient man made use of chemistry in cooking and baking, in pottery-making, tanning skins of animals, and in preparing dyes to paint his body, color his cloth, and draw pictures in his caves.

Later, when man began to use metals, he needed to know more about chemistry in order to extract the metals from their ores. It is scarcely likely that these ancients understood why certain reactions occurred. Rather, they simply chanced to notice a reaction such as a metal melting out of its ore when a very hot fire happened to be made on an ore-bearing rock. The first crude experimentation may have followed such an accidental discovery. Certainly the early Egyptians and Babylonians who made and colored glass must have had some knowledge of chemicals to be able to do so.

Little by little as the centuries passed, man was using the chemical world around him to help him advance his civilization. But his information still consisted of individual facts rather than proven broad principles. For example, he had found that when he roasted meat over a wood fire the dripping fat, mixing with the very hot ashes, made soap. Today we say that fat, either animal or vegetable, when boiled in a solution of an alkali such as sodium hydroxide or potassium hydroxide (which occur in wood ashes), gives us glycerol and soap.

The early Greeks, trying to find some explanation for what they saw in the world around them, looked for "elements" of which they supposed all matter to be composed. One of them, Empedokles, who lived in the fifth century B.C., probably borrowing an idea of the Egyptians and Hindus, suggested that all matter was made of the four "elements"—air, fire, water, and earth. His explanation was further advanced by Aristotle a hundred years later. This philosopher added the statement that there existed an unknown "prime" element from which all the other four were derived, and which could change one element into another.

Aristotle's theory of the four elements persisted throughout Europe for two thousand years. During that time, however, great strides were made in man's knowledge of chemicals as a result of the strange work of men called alchemists.

There is some question as to the origin of the word "alchemist." One theory holds that it came from the ancient name of Egypt, "Khem"; and "al", the Arabic word for "the." This theory is quite plausible, since for hundreds of years after the decline of the Greeks, Alexandria in Egypt became the center of the study of metal work. Then, when the Arabs came into Spain in great numbers, they carried with them the knowledge and skills they had learned in "al Khem"—"the Egypt"—and extended this knowledge further. In time, according to this theory, "al Khem" began to be used to mean work with metals and what we now call chemicals.

The alchemists were dedicated to what we today would consider a queer task. They were convinced that there was, as Aristotle had indicated, an "essence" of the four elements. This essence, they said, was of such extreme purity that it had the power of changing ordinary metals into gold. Moreover, they believed that this essence, which came to be called the "philosopher's stone," had a companion-essence, the "elixir of life," which could cure diseases, prolong life, and renew youth.

Thus the alchemists searched for the philosopher's stone and the elixir of life. In doing so, they examined and experimented with every imaginable chemical available to them. Some of the alchemists were most certainly charlatans who pretended to weave magic spells and tricked their patrons into believing they had changed base metals into gold. But most were hard-working men who impoverished themselves in their attempt to find the elusive philosopher's stone, a will-o'-the-wisp that somehow always remained just beyond their reach.

In performing their work, the alchemists gave fanciful, romantic names to chemicals. "Flowers of sulphur," "butter of antimony," "martial vitriol," "powder of algaroth", were only a few of them. A mystical, confusing picture of chemistry became even more so as such names kept on being added to the list. Most of the work done was by trial-and-error, rather than by true experiment. Here and there an alchemist based his work on planned experimentation, but when he tried to explain his ideas to others, no one listened to him.

Nevertheless, the alchemists were, in actual fact, the chemists of the Middle Ages and of the Renaissance. A great 17th century British philosopher, Francis Bacon, wrote of them: "Alchemy may be compared to the man who told his sons that he had left them gold buried somewhere in his vineyard; where they by digging found no gold, but by turning up the mould about the roots of the vines, procured a plentiful vintage. So the search and endeavors to make gold have brought many useful inventions and instructive experiments to light."

In the early sixteenth century, a change occurred which took many alchemists away from a search for the philosopher's stone and toward the discovery of chemicals for use in medicine. This change came about as the result of the work and teachings of the Swiss physician, Paracelsus. He attacked the goals of the alchemists violently, hammering away at them with statements like: "The true use of chemistry is not to make gold, but to prepare medicines." Many became converts to Paracelsus' teachings and turned to experimentation with chemicals, especially minerals, to be used for medicines.

Together with this new medico-chemistry came another change. Other alchemists, tired of their fruitless search for the philosopher's stone, began to give their attention to chemical industries such as smelting of ores, manufacturing ceramics and other practical uses of chemicals. Alchemy, while not completely dead, was slowly becoming a thing of the past. Even the name "alchemy" was being generally changed to "chymistry" in English and "chymie" in French, and the men engaged in this field were calling themselves "chymists."

Slowly, very slowly, other changes were taking place in the thinking of chemists. Some were questioning the theory of Aristotle's four elements as the basic material of all matter. Others, particularly the Dutch chemist, Jan van Helmont, recognized that all "air" (by which he meant gas) was not alike. He could not make clear distinctions between different "airs", possibly because he had no way of collecting them. But he is remembered, among other things, for his coining of the word "gas" from the Greek word "chaos."

It has been said that the greatest single step in changing chemistry into a true science was taken by Robert Boyle, who lived in England and Ireland from 1627 to 1691. It was Boyle who realized that chemistry must become a science in its own right, apart from medicine and alchemy. Boyle insisted on carrying out at all times a system of reasoning in chemistry based on experiment, observation, and measurement. In his book *The Sceptical Chymist,* published in 1662, he attacked the alchemists for their fuzzy thinking and the medico-chemists for the narrowness of their field. He wrote scathingly of the theory of the "four elements" of air, fire, water, and earth. Then he proceeded to define what he considered to be a true element in these words:

"I now mean by elements . . . certain primitive and simple or perfectly unmingled bodies; which not being made of any other bodies, or of one another, are the ingredients of which all those called perfectly mixed bodies are immediately compounded, and into which they are ultimately resolved." Thus Boyle, in a few concise words, gave an almost modern definition of an element as something which cannot be decomposed into anything simpler.

He also defined a compound as a substance made of two or more elements, a definition we accept today. But Boyle, hampered by the lack of chemical knowledge of his day, was unable to draw up a list of elements. Nor was his definition of an element generally accepted. The time was not ripe for such a drastic change in chemical thinking.

Another question occupying the minds of chemists at that time was that of burning, or combustion. What, indeed, in chemical terms, really happened when a substance burned? Working long hours in his laboratory Boyle tried to find out. As a result of many experiments, he concluded that air contained a vital substance necessary for burning and for the support of living things as well. Yet he did not understand what this vital substance was. His one-time assistant, Robert Hooke, went further in these experiments. However, it was John Mayow, an English physician and chemist, who proved that burning and breathing both take an *unknown something from the air*.

Here, at last, in the year 1674, was a hint of the truth about the process of burning. Unfortunately, however, these facts discovered by Boyle, Hooke, and Mayow were largely neglected due to the emergence of a new theory of combustion.

This was called the "phlogiston theory" and was first propounded by Johann Joachim Becher in the mid-17th century and later elaborated by Georg Ernst Stahl. Unhappily, the phlogiston theory, which was accepted for almost a hundred years, did chemistry a great disservice. It prevented most scientists from experimenting further to reach a true understanding of the important process of combustion.

Becher and Stahl's theory stated that all combustible

materials contained a "principle of fire" of extremely light weight which Stahl called "phlogiston." When a substance burned, the theory went on to say, it became separated from its phlogiston which was then carried away by the surrounding air. For example, since charcoal burned very easily and left so little ash, it must contain a tremendous amount of phlogiston. Thus, although air was necessary to the process of burning, its only function was to carry away phlogiston. Actually the theory made sense, because when a substance burned flames and fumes were given off, while the remaining ash weighed less than the original material.

However, the big exception to this loss of weight was the "calcination" of metals. As Robert Boyle and several others, notably the French physician Jean Rey, had discovered, metals became heavier when heated in air, or were "calcined." To explain this apparent contradiction to the phlogiston theory, chemists declared that the phlogiston contained in a metal had "negative weight." Upon the release of this weight during the heating of the metal, the calx of the metal, or as we would now say, its oxide, weighed more. In order to restore this "negative phlogiston," charcoal was added to a calx and both were heated together. The calx would then seize "negative phlogiston" from the charcoal which often disappeared, and pure metal was restored.

Yet, despite this strange theory, chemistry continued to make progress, for winds of change were blowing through all scientific thinking. Chemists were beginning to experiment with gases, but they had difficulty in working with them because they had no efficient means of collecting these "airs." Then, in 1727, the Reverend Stephen Hales invented a crude pneumatic trough for collecting a gas by displacing water. The essential part of this piece of apparatus consisted of a water-filled jar inverted over a large vessel containing more water. Gas which passed into the upper jar pushed out some of the water into the lower vessel; thus a jar of gas, or "air," could be collected. However, the apparatus was so awkward to handle that few chemists bothered to use it.

One who was not discouraged by it was Joseph Black, a Scottish physician and a well-known teacher at the Universities of Glasgow and Edinburgh. In 1756 Black published a paper telling of his discovery of an "air" different from ordinary air. He called it "fixed air" because it seemed to be "fixed" into mild alkalis. We know this gas today as carbon dioxide.

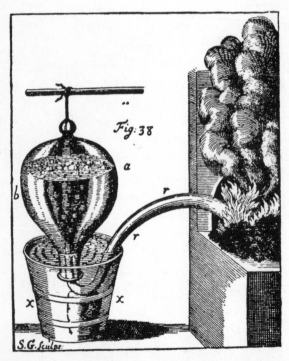

Stephen Hales' apparatus for collecting a gas, as shown in his book Vegetable Staticks.

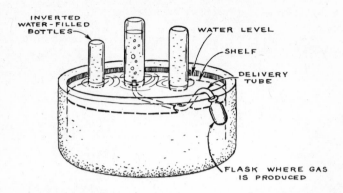

The pneumatic trough developed by Joseph Priestley for collecting a gas by displacement.

Prominent among those who occupied themselves with the study of gases was the brilliant, eccentric Englishman, Henry Cavendish. In 1766 he used an improved version of Hale's apparatus for collecting gas to discover "inflammable air"—hydrogen. Cavendish was one of the first investigators to weigh gases and to measure their densities. Another chemist, Carl Wilhelm Scheele of Sweden, found new ways of producing hydrogen, in addition to discovering important new substances.

Last of this group of chemists who were studying gases, but not the least by far, was the English clergyman, Joseph Priestley. In 1772 he perfected the pneumatic trough for collecting gases by displacing water. His trough, with but little change, is used for this same purpose today.

These three pioneer investigators, Cavendish, Scheele, and Priestley, lived and worked at the same time as Antoine-Laurent Lavoisier. Some of their most important discoveries were still to be made at the time Lavoisier started to pursue his scientific career seriously. Indeed, the paths of the two Englishmen were destined to cross his before their work was done.

LAVOISIER
AS TAX FARMER AND ACADEMICIAN

❧ SHORTLY AFTER Antoine Lavoisier had seriously embarked on a full-time scientific career, he began to consider ways of investing his inheritance profitably. He wanted to do this because he needed to be sure he would always be able to afford the best scientific equipment money could buy. After consulting with friends, Lavoisier decided to buy one-third of a share in the Tax Farm, more generally known as the Farm-General or *Ferme Générale*.

The Tax Farm was an institution peculiarly French. In effect it was a corporation to which the king "farmed out" the privilege of collecting taxes. In return, the monarch received a set sum each year in advance. Any money the Tax Farm collected beyond this sum paid to the king was divided among the shareholders.

At this time, nobles and members of the French clergy were exempt from paying any taxes, but the middle class and the poor were not. The burden, then, fell upon the commoner who saw himself being taxed heavily while the nobility lived in luxury on grants given them by the king—that is, from money received from the Tax Farm.

The Tax Farm was empowered to impose taxes on wine and many other items, and in addition, held the monopoly on the sale of tobacco and salt. The most unpopular tax levied was the one on salt, called the *gabelle*. According to French law of that period, every commoner from the age of seven paid for seven pounds of salt a year, plus the tax on it, whether the salt was actually bought or not! Besides all these taxes, any person entering Paris had to pay a toll, and this money, too, went into the treasury of the Farmers-General. Goods carried across the border from one province into another were also subject to taxation, as were goods brought into France. Understandably, then, there was such resentment among the people toward the taxes that many tried to evade paying them. Moreover, in order to collect the taxes due, agents of the Farmers-General often resorted to cruel measures against delinquents. Hatred for the whole system was usually vented on these collecting agents, for they were the only personal contact the commoner had with the Tax Farm. And against the institution itself smouldered a raw, angry resentment, only waiting to erupt to the surface.

Yet from a business point of view a share in the *Ferme Générale* was a good investment. Needless to say, the members saw to it that a good profit was left after the king's advance payment was deducted and all other expenses were met. However, the shareholders did not simply sit back and reap their profits. They were expected to serve on several committees and to work as administrators in the Paris offices of the Ferme-Générale. Each committee met frequently, assigned work to its members, and implemented the reports and suggestions made to it. When Lavoisier became a shareholder, he joined the Committee on Accounts. Many of his hours thereafter were taken up by committee work, but he did not begrudge giving up the time. After all, the profits his investment brought him were going into furnishing one of the finest laboratories in Paris.

In addition to his joining the Farmers-General, that same year—1768—Lavoisier was nominated for membership as assistant in chemistry in the Royal Academy of Science. This exclusive body was made up of fifty-four scientists and twelve assistants chosen from the various fields of science and mathematics. Elections were not held at any regular time, but only when a vacancy occurred.

The Academy had been established in 1666 by King Louis XIV as a counterpart of the Royal Society of London. Although to all practical purposes a nominee was elected by the members themselves, a recommendation was in fact submitted to the king, who made the actual appointment. There was a good reason for the king's nominal role in the affairs of the Academy, for it was the official advisory body to the state on all scientific matters. This meant that it reported to the king on such diverse subjects as the water supply of Paris, prison conditions, flight by balloons, fossils, cultivation of certain crops, the proper working of coal mines, and the weaving of tapestries. Moreover, the king paid salaries to most of the Academicians in recognition of the services they were rendering to the state.

Twice a week, on Wednesday and Saturday afternoons, the Academy met in rooms set aside for it in the old Louvre Palace near the Seine. While membership was unquestionably an honor, it was also a grave responsibility. When Lavoisier accepted the nomination he realized that, if elected, much of his time would be divided between the Farmers-General and the Academy. This would leave him comparatively little to pursue his own interests. Yet nomination at the age of twenty-five was indeed a signal honor and not to be taken lightly. Most of the members had had to wait until they were much older before being accorded such recognition.

Actually Lavoisier, at this point in his scientific career, had hardly done work important enough to warrant election to the Academy. Still, his sponsors pointed out, he had read several papers before that body, notably the excellent one on gypsum and plaster of Paris. He had in addition received a special medal from the king for his essay on street lighting, and had done exceptionally well as assistant to Guettard. Moreover, he was well known to many of the members as a former diligent pupil and now a friend. Knowing the young man, they saw in him great possibilities for future achievement as a scientist because of his singleness of purpose in wishing to advance himself. Of course, Lavoisier's financial independence helped him greatly, since, except for his work with the Farmers-General, he could devote himself exclusively to science.

On June 1, 1768, upon the recommendation of the Academy, King Louis XV appointed Antoine Lavoisier to the Royal Academy of Science as an assistant. Aunt Constance and his father were elated when they heard of the appointment. Whatever regrets Jean-Antoine may still have had at his son's change of career now evaporated in the warmth of his satisfaction with Antoine's achievements in his chosen field.

No sooner had Lavoisier been elected to the Academy than he became involved in a proposed project to furnish the city of Paris with a more adequate water supply. With the growth of the city and an increase in its population a supply of good drinking water had become a serious problem. One engineer, Antoine Deparcieux, proposed tapping the water of the nearby river Yvette and bringing it to Paris. Upon Deparcieux's death in 1768 Lavoisier was appointed by the Academy to study the engineer's plan. The more Lavoisier studied this plan the more he became convinced that it was practical. The city authorities were impressed by Lavoisier's analysis and recommendations and voted to adopt this plan; however, there was no money to carry it out. Not until almost ten years later was work even started on this project.

The young academician's investigations into a pure water supply for Paris led him naturally to other speculations about water. Suppose one had pure water, he asked himself, how long would it remain pure if left standing— even in a completely sealed glass or earthen vessel? Scientists as great as Isaac Newton had believed that upon evaporation or distillation water was partly changed into earth. In this way they accounted for the appearance of tiny particles of earth left in a vessel when water had been evaporated or distilled.

This explanation did not satisfy Lavoisier. After reading all that had been written on the subject, he felt that somewhere there was a flaw in the experiments leading to this conclusion. To determine the truth or falsity of the theory that water changed into soil, in 1768 he devised an experimental method of finding out.

First, after it had been raining for a while so that the air was free of dust, Lavoisier collected a quantity of rain water in glass vessels. Next he distilled some of this water eight times in order to make it as pure as possible. Then he weighed the amount of water he was to use, together

A pelican such as Lavoisier used for the continual distillation of water.

with the special piece of glass apparatus called a pelican that he had ordered made for the experiment. As a precaution he put the weighed water into the glass vessel, put the stopper on loosely, and gently heated the pelican to expel some of the air in it. Lavoisier knew that unless he did this, the pressure of air expanding when the container was heated for any length of time might cause the glass to break. Lastly, he sealed the pelican and weighed the water and container together.

For 101 days, beginning on October 24, the sealed pelican was heated, and the water in it distilled and continually redistilled. During the first month Lavoisier was unable to see any change in the water and was almost ready to give up the experiment altogether. But on November 20 he noticed tiny particles moving around in the water.

This was no time for discouragement, he knew, but a time for patience. In the next few weeks the tiny specks gradually became thin flakes and then settled to the bottom of the pelican.

Lavoisier was now ready to check the results of his experiment. He put out the six-wick lamp which had been heating the sand-bath in which the pelican stood and allowed the glass vessel to cool slowly. Then, with the stopper still in place, he weighed the pelican and its contents and found that there had been no change in the total weight. Nothing, then, had entered or left the vessel, so that Lavoisier knew whatever change had taken place in those 101 days must be within the water itself or the glass vessel. In this way he eliminated any outside factor that might have affected the results.

Soon Lavoisier was to know whether his suspicion that water did not change into soil was correct. Carefully he opened the pelican, poured the water and the solid particles that were in it into another glass vessel, and weighed the pelican. It had lost 17.4 grains in weight. The glass of the vessel, therefore, must have been the source of the particles found in the water being distilled. And, if this were so, the weight of the solids produced during the experiment should equal the decrease in weight of the pelican.

Lavoisier confirmed this by allowing the water used during the experiment to evaporate. He then weighed the residue left when the water dried out. Sure enough, the weight of the solids was just about the same as that lost by the glass container.

Lavoisier wrote, in his report to the Academy in May of 1769, that water did not in fact change into soil at all.

Instead, solid particles came from the action of the heated water on the glass of the vessel in which it was being distilled or evaporated. The report was lengthily entitled *On the Nature of Water and on the Experiments Alleged to Prove its Transmutability into Earth,* and published by the Academy in 1773. To this day it remains a masterpiece of the scientific thinking for which Lavoisier was becoming justly known.

MARIE ANNE PAULZE BECOMES
MADAME LAVOISIER

SEVEN

CONSIDERING THE prominent social circle into which Antoine-Laurent Lavoisier had been born, it was surprising that he took so little part in the social life of Paris. Although he did not seclude himself from the companionship of young people, neither did he actively seek it. True, he had a number of friends, but none of these was very intimate; his closest friends were, in fact, his father and his Aunt Constance. Nevertheless when Lavoisier was in the company of others, he was well-spoken, his manners were charming, and his smile was a ready one. Doubtless the reason for Lavoisier's behavior was that he found his work so time-consuming that few hours were left for lighter pursuits.

Meanwhile, the obligations imposed on Lavoisier as a

shareholder in the Farmers-General were many. In the first few years after making his initial investment—he now owned a full share—Lavoisier was asked to undertake many tours of inspection, and these often took him away from Paris. Upon his return there were reports to write and meetings to attend. In addition, the laboratory in the rue de Four-Saint-Eustache claimed his attention, as did the Academy. During these years, too, Lavoisier had retained his interest in air pressure and its relation to the weather. Records of this, together with those he was receiving from correspondents in other parts of Europe, had to be arranged and noted in his journal. Little wonder then that Lavoisier, although still in his twenties, took slight interest in Paris society. And little wonder, either, that he had not yet married. As it happened, the chance that placed Lavoisier as assistant to the Farmer-General, Jacques Paulze, also brought him a wife.

In the France of Lavoisier's day, it was common practice for parents to arrange a marriage of convenience for their children, so as to conserve or even increase the family wealth. However, thoughtful parents took pains to consider the personal likes and dislikes of their son or daughter, and the suitability of the suggested marriage partner.

In the fall of 1771 Jacques Paulze's daughter, Marie, was not quite fourteen years old, pretty, vivacious, blue-eyed and auburn-haired. Because her father was well-to-do she would someday receive a considerable sum of money for her marriage settlement, and would eventually inherit still more. Paulze was approached that autumn by his late wife's uncle, the French Minister of Finance Abbé Terray, with the idea of arranging a marriage between Marie and a certain nobleman, the Count d'Amerval. The Abbé was

acting as intermediary at the request of his friend the
Baroness de la Garde, sister of the Count.

Marie's father was appalled at the thought of such a
marriage for his young daughter, even though it meant she
would marry into the nobility. He reflected that the Count
d'Amerval was fifty years old, and penniless, while Marie
was not yet fourteen. It seemed to Paulze that the Baroness de la Garde must therefore be pressing the match for
her brother only to recoup his fortunes. In return, she
offered the alluring prospect of a title and a gay life at
court to the motherless girl. Still, to displease Abbé Terray,
who as Minister of Finance had a powerful control over
the shareholders in the Tax Farm, was not prudent, either.
What was he to do?

In talking the situation over with his daughter, Paulze
learned that she disliked the Count intensely, and that in
her eyes he was, in her own words, "a fool, stupid and ill-
mannered, a kind of ogre." She would have none of him.
On learning of Marie's feelings her father wrote to her
great-uncle explaining why he considered the proposed
match unsuitable, and added, "My daughter has a decided
objection to him; I will certainly not force her against her
wishes."

But Terray did not give up the idea of the marriage of
his grand-niece to his friend's brother. Paulze knew, then,
that pressure on him would be increased; the best solution
would be to arrange a good marriage for Marie as quickly
as possible. In casting about in his mind for a suitable husband for his daughter, his thoughts rested on his assistant,
Antoine Lavoisier.

If both young people agreed, Paulze thought, this could
be a perfect match. Neither one needed to marry for

money; both were intelligent and came from fine, cultured homes. Marie, moreover, was receiving a better education than most girls of the time, so that she would make a good intellectual companion for a man like Lavoisier. For these reasons Paulze decided to broach the subject of marriage between the two separately, to his daughter and to his young assistant in the Tax Farm.

Marie had already met Lavoisier at her home, and had been favorably impressed with his appearance, his manner, and his intelligence. Most certainly, the young girl thought, he was not a stupid fool nor an ill-mannered ogre; nor was he after her money, for his wealth was greater than hers. Marie had no objection to marrying Antoine Lavoisier if he, too, wished it. For his part Lavoisier, who until now had not thought seriously of marriage, was pleased and honored to be considered a proper husband for so charming and accomplished a girl as Marie Paulze. Although she was half his age, he consented eagerly to the match.

As was the custom, the fathers of the two young people met to arrange details of the marriage settlement. All was quickly arranged, and at a grand reception on December 4, 1771, the marriage contract between Marie-Anne-Pierrette Paulze and Antoine-Laurent Lavoisier was signed. Among the guests, and the first witness to sign the contract, was of course Aunt Constance. Also present were members of the Academy, the Farmers-General, scientists, and statesmen. The Abbé Terray, too, accepted his disappointment gracefully and came to the reception. To show that he held no ill-will toward the young bride-to-be and her father, he asked that the wedding be held in his own private chapel.

Less than two weeks later, on December 16, 1771, Marie

Paulze became the wife of Antoine Lavoisier in her great-uncle's chapel in the rue Neuve des Petits-Champs. A house in the rue Neuve des Bons-Enfants, given to Lavoisier by his father as a wedding gift, became the home of the newly-married couple. Soon after, just before the end of the year, Jean-Antoine gave his son and new daughter-in-law another gift, a patent of nobility which he had bought for Antoine. A patent of nobility, for sale by the royal treasury, conferred upon its holders the right to be considered a nobleman, and with it to add "de" before the family name. Antoine, while thanking his father graciously, never took advantage of this privilege. He never called himself "de Lavoisier," but considered himself a commoner all of his life.

The new Mme. Lavoisier gladly relinquished the task of household management to Aunt Constance, who had come to live with them. Freed from the immediate necessity of directing her household, Marie set herself the more difficult task of further educating herself to keep pace with her brilliant husband. Her first concern was to be of some help to Antoine in his scientific work and, with this in mind, she undertook to study Latin and English. She chose these two languages because Latin was still being used to some extent in scholarly writings. And a knowledge of English had become most useful for a chemist, for some very important work in chemistry was being done in England. Therefore Marie decided to learn at least enough to be able to translate for Antoine papers and books from the English, since Lavoisier himself unfortunately knew no language except French.

There were other things Marie Lavoisier wanted to study, too. She realized that in order to be able to translate chemical papers intelligently she would have to learn some chemistry. Possibly to make drawings to illustrate her husband's reports, and certainly to develop her own considerable artistic talent, she also studied painting and engraving. Nor did she neglect to continue to play the piano, for Antoine, too, enjoyed playing it.

What had started out as a marriage of convenience rather than a love match turned out to be one of the happiest and most fortunate unions in the history of science.

THE FIRST STEP
TOWARD THE CHEMICAL REVOLUTION

EIGHT

※ AFTER HIS MARRIAGE Antoine Lavoisier's happiness reflected itself in the renewed zeal with which he resumed his chemical experimentation. Indeed, the year 1772 has been called "the crucial year" in determining the direction his work was to take, for investigations both in England and in France finally turned him to the study of air and its role in burning, or combustion.

The first of these was the investigation of the "disappearing diamonds." As early as 1768 the French chemist Jean Darcet had reported to the Academy that in one of his experiments two diamonds had disappeared completely after having been subjected to intense heat. Yet diamonds had always been thought to be indestructible by fire. In the exciting discussions that followed Darcet's account, it was recalled that there had been earlier reports from other parts of Europe about the disappearance of diamonds under similar circumstances. No one, however, had paid much attention to these reports. Now, encouraged by the Academy, scientists sought to discover the truth about this phenomenon.

Darcet repeated his experiment in 1770, in public demonstrations in 1771, and again early in 1772. Other scientists duplicated Darcet's work. One such public demonstration was conducted before a large audience in the presence of the Lieutenant-General of Police with the hope that any possible fraud might more easily be detected. As a result of these experiments, several theories were advanced to explain just what happened to a diamond to cause it to disappear when heated. To settle the question once and for all, the Academy appointed a committee to experiment and to submit a report on its findings. The committee, consisting of Pierre-Joseph Macquer, Louis Claude Cadet, and Antoine-Laurent Lavoisier, went to work in Cadet's laboratory since it was the best equipped for that purpose.

The result of the first experiment was inconclusive and another was suggested to see if a diamond would be destroyed in complete absence of air. But diamonds were expensive and the experimenters were unwilling to buy one with the possibility that it would be destroyed. When a jeweler called Maillard learned of the proposed experiment, he came to their aid. Maillard was so convinced that diamonds disappear only when heated in the presence of air that he offered them the use of three diamonds for their experiment. The only condition he made was that he be allowed to set up the experiment to satisfy himself that no air could come in contact with the precious stones.

The chemists agreed. On the appointed day Maillard embedded the diamonds in the bowl of a clay pipe filled with powdered charcoal. Then he sealed the pipe with more clay and cemented it inside two crucibles, one inverted over the other to form a nest. Finally he cemented the crucibles together. This done, the chemists were permitted to heat the crucibles in their furnace. After hours of intense heat, they removed the apparatus and broke out the diamonds. The stones had not lost even a fraction of their weight and, except for a slight darkening of their surface, had otherwise remained unchanged.

In his report to the Academy on April 29, 1772, presented on behalf of the whole committee, Lavoisier wrote that a diamond, if protected from the air, cannot be affected by heat. He suggested the possibility that a diamond actually burns up when heated to extreme temperatures in the presence of air, but that his committee as yet had no absolute proof of this. The committee then agreed upon further experiments to be conducted later in the summer which might reveal the whole truth of the matter.

This speculation on the role that air played in making a diamond burn only added to Lavoisier's recent determination to experiment on the entire problem of air and the part it played in chemistry. A number of incidents, coming swiftly one after another, had served to arouse his interest in just this problem of air and burning.

One of these was the publication, in the late spring of 1772, of a book by Louis-Bernard Guyton de Morveau, a lawyer and chemist from Dijon. In his book de Morveau described in great detail experiments he had done with metals. His investigations proved beyond a doubt that all known metals capable of being calcined gained weight when they underwent that process. De Morveau could not explain this phenomenon except in terms of a strange distortion of the phlogiston theory. But Lavoisier, on reading de Morveau's explanation, began to question it. It seemed clear to him that air was in some way involved in changing a metal from its pure form to its calx. Was it possible that metals actually absorbed air during calcination? Could this account for the increase in weight of a calx, rather than the "negative phlogiston" theory of metals?

Another link in the chain leading Lavoisier to his study of the role air played in chemistry was a letter written to him in July by a friend, Trudaine de Montigny. In it de Montigny said he had just learned that the British chemist Joseph Priestley had succeeded in making artificial Seltzer water and was suggesting its use for medicinal purposes. Trudaine enclosed a copy in English of Priestley's report, *Directions for Impregnating Water with Fixed Air* and suggested that Lavoisier translate it into French and try these experiments for himself.

But Lavoisier knew no English, nor had his wife as yet learned enough to undertake the task of translation. Later, when Priestley's *Directions* were translated into French and published early in August in the scientific journal of Abbé Francois Rozier, Lavoisier read it eagerly. He, like other French chemists, knew comparatively little about the chemistry of gases, for Englishmen had far outstripped all others in that branch of science.

As Lavoisier studied Priestley's method of making Seltzer water, he considered the whole question of effervescence, or bubbling of gases as they escape. He recalled that his first chemistry teacher, Rouelle, had often spoken of the work of an earlier English chemist, Stephen Hales. In an attempt to clarify his ideas about effervescence, Lavoisier turned once more to the work of Hales, particularly to his book *Vegetable Staticks* published in 1727.

Hales had described a number of experiments which had convinced him that air was in some manner fixed in all animal or vegetable substances, and in many other materials besides. He drew attention as well as the fact that the calx of a metal effervesces when being reduced to its pure metal. The British chemist had even succeeded in measuring the amount of air released or absorbed in many chemical reactions. But, Hales believed, air simply mixed with these substances, without causing any chemical change.

Lavoisier's keen mind immediately made a connection between the effervescence of the calx of metals when being reduced, as noticed by Hales, and de Morveau's proof of their gain in weight upon calcination. Could it be that one was the reverse of the other? Did air *combine chemically* with a metal when it was heated, and so add to the weight of the metal? And, when a metal was recovered from its calx, was the release of air responsible for the ensuing loss of weight? If this were indeed so, what then happened to the phlogiston? Perhaps the whole phlogiston theory itself needed to be changed.

These were the questions that plagued Lavoisier during the summer of 1772, and he was impatient to experiment further in the hope of finding answers to them. In particular, he was eager to experiment with the calx of lead—lead oxide—known in Lavoisier's time as litharge, or red lead. This chemical had been used by many other chemists in the study of the effect of heat on calces, and Lavoisier wanted to verify some of their findings. But he needed intense heat concentrated on the red lead to reduce it quickly enough for him to collect any gas, or "air," given off. Neither the furnace, nor any other means he had been using to obtain heat suited this purpose. Then he remembered the great Tschirnhausen burning-lens that, unused for many years, had been gathering dust in the curio cabinet of the Academy. This lens, which was thirty-three feet in diameter, had the ability to focus the intense heat of the sun on a small area. Thus an experimenter could obtain more concentrated heat than from a furnace or from a battery of oil lamps.

However, before Lavoisier could proceed with his own work, there still remained the problem of the "disappearing diamonds" to be resolved. He now began to wonder if an improvement in the techniques the committee members had used would bring more conclusive results. If, for example, the precious stones were subjected to a much greater heat than was possible from a wood or charcoal furnace, would they break into tiny pieces, simply evaporate, or burn up altogether?

To find out, Lavoisier received permission for the committee to use the old Tschirnhausen burning-lens for their diamond experiments. In addition, another lens of equal diameter but with a shorter focal length was lent to the experimenters by its owner, the Comte de la Tour d'Auvergne. With the two largest and most powerful lenses ever made, the scientists began a series of experiments in the middle of August.

They set up their lenses in the Jardin de l'Infante, a terrace in the garden of the old Louvre Palace. A ground floor apartment of the palace was placed at their disposal to house the lenses and other equipment. First they experi-

A burning lens similar to the one used by Lavoisier in his diamond experiments. (Courtesy of Denis I. Duveen)

mented with a variety of metals and mineral substances, and then with the diamonds.

In this last experiment, which was conducted during the first week in October, Lavoisier suggested that once and for all they settle the question of whether the diamonds disappear. The committee agreed to his proposal that they try to burn the diamonds in air with the aid of the great lens, and that any gas given off be collected and tested. They then placed several small diamonds in a fine porcelain crucible and arranged apparatus for collecting any resulting gases. The intense heat of the noonday sun was focused on the diamonds—and in twenty minutes they vanished! But this time the scientists, even as the diamonds became smaller and smaller and then disappeared, had succeeded in collecting a gas. They tested this gas and found it to be "fixed air", the same gas given off when charcoal burns, a gas we know today as carbon dioxide.

Thus the scientists in the Jardin de l'Infante finally accepted the fact that a diamond actually burns when subjected to heat in the presence of air. Lavoisier was asked to compile all the committee's findings for presentation to the Academy. This report is still in existence in the archives of the French Academy of Science.

The results of the committee's investigation gave Lavoisier much to think about. He reasoned that if the gas produced by the burning diamond was "fixed air," then a diamond might be a kind of carbon. It might, in fact, be considered a fuel. And, since all fuels burned only in the presence of air, was it not possible that *air itself* contained some special property necessary for burning, aside and apart from phlogiston? Perhaps by experimenting he would find out.

With the experiments on the diamonds ended, the great Tschirnhausen burning-lens was now available for Lavoisier's own use. Yet he had not waited idly by until it was free before exploring some of his ideas further. During August and into early fall, he had tried some experiments with two common non-metallic chemicals, phosphorus and sulphur, in order to see if they gained weight upon burning. The British chemist Hales had noted that phosphorus did gain weight, but had offered no explanation for this contradiction of the phlogiston theory. Lavoisier now decided to test Hale's findings for himself, since the whole question of the gain or loss of weight of a chemical upon combustion had become all-important to him.

Invariably, when phosphorus was burned in a closed vessel, Lavoisier's results showed it absorbed large amounts of air. The burned phosphorus always weighed more than the original chemical, and this gain was about equal to the weight of the air that had been absorbed. When sulphur was heated in contact with a measured amount of air, it reacted in the same way, except that a heavy gas was formed. Again, the gas weighed as much as the sulphur plus the air lost in the container.

Lavoisier was thus able to show that phosphorus and sulphur gained weight by actually *combining* with air when they burned. It remained for him to prove, as he suspected, that this was also true of metals when they became calcined. Guyton de Morveau's earlier observations might then receive their correct interpretation. The reduction of litharge, the calx of lead, to its pure metal and the weighing of the gas released, could possibly give him the answer.

LAVOISIER'S FIRST BOOK IS
PUBLISHED

NINE

In mid-October, using the big burning-lens, Antoine Lavoisier started his experiments with litharge. He adapted a pedestal apparatus first used by Stephen Hales, so that he could make a more exact measurement of any air given off. It consisted of a basin of water into which was fixed a crystal pedestal topped by a porcelain crucible. He put a weighed amount of red lead and a piece of charcoal in the crucible and inverted a crystal bell jar over the basin and the pedestal. Then, when he sucked out some of the air from the bell jar with a tube, water rose in the jar to take the place of the air just removed. Lastly, he skimmed a layer of oil over the surface of the water so that any gas given off would not be dissolved in the water, and marked its level with adhesive paper.

Now Lavoisier focused the rays of the sun on the litharge. When the red lead became heated he noticed the level of the water in the jar falling rapidly as a considerable amount of gas was released. When all the litharge had turned to pure lead, he was able to estimate this amount

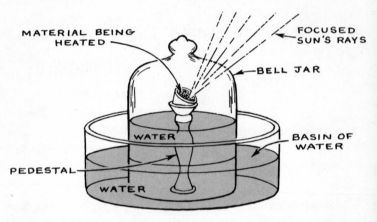

The pedestal apparatus.

of gas and to test it. He found that the gas was "fixed air," the same gas Priestley had used in making his Seltzer water. By this time Lavoisier may very well have suspected that the "air" lost by the lead was being used by the charcoal to make the "fixed air," but nowhere did he say so at that time.

To be certain that the result of his experiment with lead was not accidental, he repeated it several times, and each time the same gas was given off. Combining these results with those he had observed in the burning of phosphorus and sulphur, Lavoisier now reached the daring conclusion that all non-metallic substances absorbed air when they burned, and that metals did so when they were calcined. And, since the phlogiston theory in no way could account for this, it was very possible that the hundred-year-old theory itself was incorrect. But to state so publicly would be unwise until he had further facts to substantiate his own growing convictions regarding the part air played in combustion. Nevertheless, so much experimentation was being done with air by both English and French chemists that Lavoisier thought it quite possible some one else might come to the same conclusion he had. Therefore, in order to show he had been the first to make this dis-covery, Lavoisier deposited a sealed note, dated Novem-ber 1, 1772, with the secretary of the Academy. In it he described briefly his experiments in burning phosphorus and sulphur, and in reducing litharge to lead. He wrote in this note:

"About eight days ago I discovered that sulphur, in burning, far from losing weight, on the contrary gains it; . . . it is the same with phosphorus; this increase of weight arises from a prodigious quantity of air that is fixed during the combustion and combines with the vapors. This dis-covery, which I have established by experiments that I regard as decisive, has led me to think that what is observed in the combustion of sulphur and phosphorus may well take place in the case of all substances that gain in weight by combustion and calcination; and I am persuaded that the increase in weight of metallic calces is due to the same cause . . . This discovery appearing to me one of the most interesting of those that have been made since the time of Stahl, I felt that I ought to secure my right to it by depositing this note in the hands of the secretary of the

Academy, to remain sealed until the time when I shall make my experiments known."

With his sealed note safe in the hands of the secretary of the Academy, Lavoisier proceeded to check and recheck his experiments. Thus, should he detect any errors in the conclusions stated in the note, he could recover it and make necessary changes. Meanwhile, if he were correct, he had established priority to the discovery of a new theory of burning and calcination.

On February 20, 1773, Lavoisier made a memorandum in his laboratory notebook that was both historic and prophetic. In it he stated that he proposed to engage in a long series of experiments on the "elastic fluid"—gas— which is released in many chemical reactions and which is absorbed in the combustion of a great number of substances. He therefore thought it would be well for him to put some of his thoughts in writing, in order for him to follow a workable plan.

After a brief account of the work of Hales, Black, Priestley, and others regarding air taken in and air released from chemical reactions, he noted that not enough experimentation had as yet been done to form an acceptable theory. In the following words Lavoisier predicted where his own discoveries might lead:

"The importance of the end in view prompted me to undertake all this work, which seemed to me destined to bring about a revolution in physics and in chemistry . . . The results of other authors whom I have named, appeared to me like separate pieces of a great chain; these authors have joined only some links of the chain. But an immense series of experiments remains to be made in order to lead to a continuous whole."

Lavoisier went to work in his laboratory, tirelessly performing experiments in burning and in calcination and reduction of metals. By the beginning of May, 1773, he felt he had enough evidence to answer any criticism of the statements made in his sealed note of the previous November. At his request, the note was opened and read before the Academy on May 5.

It proved to be the first major document to help establish the fact that air combines chemically with a substance during combustion and calcination. One important fact, however, was not mentioned—that only a *certain part* of the air is used in these two processes. There was a good reason for this omission. Neither Lavoisier nor any other chemist of the time knew, as we do today, that air is a mixture of several different gases, each with its own characteristics. This knowledge was the missing piece that had to be discovered before the puzzle of combustion could be solved.

The great interest and discussion that the reading of the note provoked led Lavoisier to a decision to collect all his notes on gases into one book. He was probably impelled to do so as quickly as possible by the translation into French that year of another of Joseph Priestley's works.

This famous English chemist had already perfected a most convenient means of collecting a gas by displacing water—the pneumatic trough. In addition Priestley had discovered a way to make the artificial Seltzer water or "soda water" that Trudaine de Montigny had urged Lavoisier in July of 1772 to try for himself. And in 1772 Priestley, in experimenting with gas given off by growing mint, had shown that a candle burns more brightly in it. Priestley knew little else about this gas released by growing mint, except that a live mouse, sealed in a jar of it, lived longer than it would have done in ordinary air.

In that same year of 1772, while Lavoisier had been working so hard to find out what the connection was between air and burning, Priestley's first book on gases was published in England. It was called *Experiments and Observations on Different Kinds of Air,* and contained all that the English chemist had accomplished with gases up to that time.

When Priestley's *Observations* appeared in Paris in 1773, Lavoisier went to work feverishly to complete his own book. He did this as much to redeem the prestige of French chemistry as for his own satisfaction. His *Opus-. cules Physiques Et Chimiques—Physical and Chemical Essays*—came off the press in January, 1774.

As he had done in his notebook memorandum, Lavoisier first gave in his *Opuscules* a historical account of what had been done by earlier experimenters with "airs." Then he proceeded with details of the experiments he had mentioned briefly in his sealed note of November, 1772, and of those he had performed since. He again emphasized that he was inclined to think it was common air that mixed with a metal to form its calx, and gave his reasons for believing so. Possibly, he added, it might be a gas contained in the air that did this.

One other statement Lavoisier made in describing experiments with the burning of phosphorus proved later to be very important. He wrote that only a definite amount of phosphorus could burn in a given quantity of air in a sealed container. In these experiments the volume of air was reduced by about one-fifth, and then burning ceased. Even if he introduced fresh phosphorus into the same jar,

OPUSCULES
PHYSIQUES
ET CHYMIQUES,

Par M. LAVOISIER, de l'Académie
Royale des Sciences.

TOME PREMIER

A PARIS,

Chez {
DURAND neveu, Libraire, rue Galande.
DIDOT le jeune, quai des Augustins.
ESPRIT, au Palais Royal.
}

M. DCC. LXXIV.

Title page of Opuscules Physiques et Chymiques. (*Courtesy Rare Books Division, New York Public Library*)

it would not burn. But Lavoisier at that time offered no explanation for this phenomenon.

In reality *Opuscules Physiques et Chimiques* was an expansion of notes and memoranda Lavoisier had written for the Academy, Abbé Rozier's journal, and of his own notebooks. It served the purpose, however, of gathering all this information into one book.

Two copies of *Opuscules* were dispatched to America to Benjamin Franklin of Philadelphia. One of these, Lavoisier wrote in his letter to Franklin, was to be for his own library, and the other for the American Philosophical Society in his city. The choice of Franklin as a representative of American scientists was prompted by Franklin's election in 1772 to membership in the Academy as a foreign member for his work on electricity. Thus began a correspondence between the young French chemist and the older American statesman-scientist, and a friendship of lasting duration.

With *Opuscules* completed, Lavoisier turned to a still more thorough investigation of the problem of combustion and calcination. The more he thought about the part phlogiston was said to play in these processes, the less he was inclined to believe it. He was a scientist who weighed, measured, added and subtracted, used his eyes and other senses to detect substances. How could he then, in all honesty to himself, believe in something that was invisible and weightless, or even worse, was supposed to have "negative weight"? And similarly, how could there be such an indefinite thing as the "principle of fire"? In his search for the truth, Lavoisier now turned to books written before the phlogiston theory had been propounded, and came upon an interesting experiment done by Robert Boyle more than a hundred years earlier.

Boyle, too, had tried to solve the mystery of fire, burning, and calcination. In one of his attempts to do so he had weighed a piece of tin, sealed it in a retort, and weighed metal and container. After heating the retort for several hours he noticed the tin had become calcined. He removed the retort, cooled it, and broke open the neck to remove the tin calx. As he did so he noticed that air rushed into the retort with a hissing sound. Upon weighing the calx Boyle found it weighed more than the original metal. And, the calx plus the opened retort weighed more than they had when they were sealed. Boyle gave what to us is a strange interpretation of this fact. He said that fire, or the "soul of fire," had passed through the glass to cause the increased weight of the calx.

Lavoisier, in reading of Boyle's experiment, found a major flaw in it. How could one tell that something had entered the sealed vessel through the glass unless the sealed vessel and its contents were weighed *before the seal was broken and air rushed in?* Also, if air did rush in as the earlier English chemist had said, what had happened to the air originally in the retort? Lavoisier therefore decided to repeat Boyle's experiment, but to weigh the sealed vessel and its contents both before and after calcination.

This he proceeded to do in several different experiments, using both tin and lead. Each time the sealed retort and its contents weighed the same before it had been heated as after the metal had been calcined. Then, when he broke the neck of the retort, air rushed in with the same kind of hissing noise Boyle had noticed. The metal, then, had taken air or some part of it from the retort in the process of calcination—and this must account for the increased weight of the calx.

To conclude his experiment, Lavoisier weighed the

opened retort which was now filled with fresh air, together with the calx. He found the total weight had increased, and by the same amount as the increase of the calx alone. Here was the necessary verification that he, as a true experimental scientist, needed to have. The increase in the weight of the calx was due to air taken from the sealed retort. Another piece in the solution of the puzzle of calcination of metals had fallen into place.

Nor were tin and lead the only metals that claimed Lavoisier's attention in his experiments. Another was mercury, or quicksilver, a silvery metal that had fascinated both alchemists and chemists because of its peculiar properties. It was the one metal known to exist as a liquid at ordinary room temperatures. The calx of this metal was a heavy red powder which could easily be reduced to its original quicksilver when heated with charcoal. As was then believed, the charcoal restored "phlogiston" to it.

In February of 1774, the French chemist Pierre Bayen had been able for the first time to reduce red mercury calx to pure liquid mercury without the use of charcoal. Again, Lavoisier thought, where did the phlogiston enter into this process? The reduction of mercury without charcoal would bear looking into further. Indeed, the more Lavoisier pondered over the whole phlogiston theory the more he began to suspect that it might not be true.

Still another substance that became the subject of Lavoisier's experimentation was the gas then known as "inflammable air"—now called hydrogen. Because he was constantly seeking confirmation of his belief that something from the air was added to a burning substance, Lavoisier burned small amounts of every chemical possible. However, burning "inflammable air" pointed to a contradiction, the only one he was able to find. This gas *lost* weight when burned, or so he thought. For years this contradiction disturbed him, although it did not cause him to change the theory that was slowly forming in his mind. What Lavoisier did not know until years later was that when hydrogen burns, water is formed. The water vapor produced by the burning of his "inflammable air" was escaping into the atmosphere before he could perceive it!

❧

A FATEFUL
MEETING WITH JOSEPH PRIESTLEY

❧ MEANWHILE, MARIE LAVOISIER had not been idle. She was progressing rapidly in her study of English and had already learned enough chemistry to be able to record many of her husband's laboratory notes. Antoine found it pleasant to discuss his chemical labors with her, for Marie's quick mind easily grasped the meaning of what he was trying to say. Her ability to draw, too, had become very useful in making sketches of his laboratory set-ups.

In addition to these accomplishments Marie had also turned into a poised and charming hostess. The Lavoisier home had in this short time become a gathering place for important figures in art and literature, as well as science. This was not surprising, for in her father's house Marie had been accustomed to meeting accomplished and educated men and women. Now, as mistress in her own home, she extended invitations to such people to be her guests and, thereby, made for Lavoisier a home that was the envy of many.

In October of 1774 the Lavoisiers entertained a most welcome and distinguished guest. This was none other than Joseph Priestley, the famous British chemist. At this time, Priestley was secretary to Lord Shelburne, who was in Paris on a visit. Here was an opportunity for these two eminent scientists to meet and exchange ideas. Marie promptly arranged a small party, with Priestley as guest of honor.

The unpretentious Englishman from Yorkshire was charmed by his seventeen-year-old hostess and by his polished, sophisticated, thoughtful host. However, trying to carry on a conversation presented some difficulties, for Lavoisier spoke barely any English. As for Priestley, he spoke poor French and was a stutterer into the bargain. Try as Lavoisier might to follow Priestley's words, he soon had to depend on Marie to act as an interpreter.

Priestley was very enthusiastic about some experiments he had conducted on August 1 of that year and began to tell of them. He described how, in trying out a new burning lens, he had first heated red calx of mercury. In doing so he had been able to collect a strange, hitherto unknown gas. When he lowered a lighted candle into this gas, the flame burned with extraordinary brightness, and when he put a glowing splint of wood into the new "air," it burst into flame.

According to Priestley, the new "air" apparently had so extremely little phlogiston of its own that it seized some from whatever source it could. Hence it caused phlogiston

to escape rapidly from burning substances with the resulting brilliant flame. Therefore, Priestley told Lavoisier, he
was considering calling this new air "dephlogisticated air"
—air devoid of phlogiston.

By means of gestures, diagrams, and Marie's interpretation, Lavoisier slowly began to understand what Priestley
was describing. Suddenly a thought leaped to his mind.
Was it possible that Priestley in a haphazard way had
stumbled upon the missing link in the mystery of burning?
Could it be his "air devoid of phlogiston" that combined
with chemicals in combustion and in metals when they
were calcined? He hid his excitement at the prospect of
such a possibility, but exchanged a meaningful glance
with his wife. Did she, too, realize the possible significance
of Priestley's discovery?

When Priestley left the house on the rue Neuve des
Bons-Enfants he had unknowingly planted a great idea in
Lavoisier's mind. The French chemist had decided to
obtain some of Priestley's new "air" in the same way the
Englishman had done, and then see if this gas might be
the last piece needed to solve the puzzle of the combustion
process.

Lavoisier's laboratory notebooks show that almost immediately after Priestley's visit he went to work to separate
the strange "air" from mercury calx. He performed many
experiments in his methodical way to be sure nothing was
overlooked that would invalidate his results.

Meanwhile, however, he could not neglect various matters of the Farmers-General and of the Academy in which
he was involved. True, he often resented the time he gave
up to committee work and writing reports for these two
organizations, but when he finally retired to his laboratory

the lost time became only a minor irritation. Then he would forget everything but the work at hand and, with Marie acting as his secretary, he pressed forward with his experiments on the separation of Priestley's "air" from mercury calx.

In England, meanwhile, Priestley had in March of 1775 experimented with the effects of this new "air" on living things. He had placed a mouse in a jar containing this "air" and found that the little animal did not begin to show signs of distress until after half an hour, although a similar mouse died in fifteen minutes in a jar of ordinary air. On March 15 he read a paper before the Royal Society of London, in which he gave an account of how he had separated this gas from mercury calx, and what its properties were. He stated that "it is five or six times better than common air, for the purpose of respiration, inflammation, and, I believe, every other use of common, atmospherical air. As I think I have sufficiently proved, that the fitness of the air for respiration depends on its capacity to receive phlogiston exhaled from the lungs, this species may not improperly be called dephlogisticated air." Thus, for the first time in any official publication, Priestley called his new gas "dephlogisticated air"—a most awkward name for a gas we know today as oxygen!

Lavoisier, learning of Priestley's experiments in proving "dephlogisticated air" highly "respirable" or breathable, repeated these experiments and confirmed Priestley's findings. He was now ready to submit his own report on the new "air" to the Academy.

On April 26, 1775 Lavoisier presented before the Academy a paper entitled *On the Nature of the Principle which Combines with the Metals During Their Calcination and*

Increases their Weight. In this paper he related how he had obtained a gas by heating the calx of mercury to a high temperature. He described the gas as "common air in an eminently pure state." This air had the ability to calcine metals and make flames burn more brightly; and, it was highly respirable.

Nowhere in this account did Lavoisier say that Joseph Priestley had told him the previous October of how he had discovered this new "air" by heating calx of mercury. In fact, he did not mention Priestley's name at all. To Lavoisier's discredit, he gave the impression that he alone was responsible for the discovery of the new "air" and of its properties.

We do not know why Lavoisier acted in this way. It is quite possible he felt that he himself had been so very close to the discovery when he met Priestley. He may have believed that even if he had not known of the Englishman's experiments, he would soon have come upon a similar discovery himself. Besides, Lavoisier may have reasoned, Priestley was so steeped in the phlogiston theory that he had no true understanding of the part this new gas played in combustion and calcination.

And, strange to say, neither Priestley nor Lavoisier were aware at that time that the Swedish chemist Carl Wilhelm Scheele had probably already discovered this new "air." Scheele did not publish any information about his discovery until 1777. Only then, several years after the announcements of the other two chemists' work, did the Swedish scientist's published laboratory notes show he had very likely discovered this new "air" before either Lavoisier or Priestley.

At any rate, it was not until 1782 that Lavoisier wrote

anywhere of Priestley's connection with the "eminently pure air." Then, he started a description of the gas with these words: "The air, which Priestley and Scheele discovered at very nearly the same time as I, and I believe even before me . . ." Although among most chemists Priestley was considered to be the discoverer of the "eminently pure air" it took Lavoisier seven years to grudgingly afford Priestley that recognition.

The memorandum on "eminently pure air", when added to the earlier *Opuscules Physiques et Chimiques,* showed a whole new pattern of thought concerning combustion and calcination. It was a pattern entirely strange to the chemists of that time. True, Lavoisier had not openly denied the existence of phlogiston, yet his experiments described in both of these works were certainly pointing to such a denial. In considering this, scientists began to examine the phlogiston theory more closely. Many of them thought that perhaps Lavoisier was on the track of something very significant on the age-old question of burning. His work therefore would bear close watching.

LAVOISIER ACCEPTS PUBLIC OFFICE

WHILE ANTOINE LAVOISIER had been so busy those last twelve months, both in his laboratory and with other business, momentous events had been taking place in France. In May, 1774, King Louis XV had died and his twenty-year-old grandson, Louis XVI, had succeeded to the throne.

Stout, placid, slow-moving and slow-thinking, Louis XVI presented a figure hard to imagine as representing the royal glory of France. He would probably have been happier as a locksmith than a king. Indeed, the locksmith shop he had installed in one of the upper floors of the palace at Versailles became his refuge when affairs of state became too burdensome. The young Austrian-born queen, Marie Antoinette, was the exact opposite of His Royal Highness. She was slight, quick, gay, extravagant, fond of play-acting, partying, and even gambling.

74

In addition to the throne, Louis had inherited a mountain of debts left him by his predecessors, as well as a most inefficient system of administering the government. The royal treasury was almost empty and, to add to his difficulties, the queen's constant demands for money knew no bounds. Obviously, the whole tottering financial structure of France needed drastic rebuilding, but unfortunately Louis was hardly the man for the job.

And what of France herself, and her people?

The French population was divided into three classes, or "estates." The first estate was made up of the members of the clergy who were exempt from taxation. In fact, they themselves collected tithes, or a ten percent tax, from farmers, merchants, and working people. Actually, most of the high-ranking clergymen performed few of the duties of their office. Rather, they lived a worldly life very different from the true purpose of their religious calling. As a result, it usually fell upon the poor parish priests to care for the spiritual needs of the people. Although they were basically religious, it was little wonder that the people of France regarded the higher clergy with cynicism and distrust.

The second estate consisted of the king and the nobility, who were also exempt from all taxation. Frequently the nobles owned great estates which they seldom visited, but from which they collected handsome profits and taxes. True, some of the noblemen were considerate, fine managers of their estates, but most tended to live a riotous life in Paris or in the royal court at Versailles. Moreover, patents of nobility could be bought for a fat fee by those who were not members of the second estate. These patents of nobility exempted their owners from the payment of taxes as though they were noblemen. In fact, it was just such a patent that Lavoisier's father had bought for Antoine and of which the scientist never took advantage.

To maintain the first and second estates the burden of taxation fell upon the rest of the population, the third estate. Peasants, city workers, businessmen, merchants, lawyers, doctors, and other professionals fell into this class unless they were of the nobility. About ninety-five percent of the people were members of the third estate.

Added to these taxes was also the hated *corvée,* the obligation of the third estate to maintain the roads and bridges of France. At a time when they were most needed to work on their farms, many of the peasants were called upon to work on the roads. The wealthier among them could buy their way out of this obligation by paying a tax instead of actually fulfilling their *corvée* duties. The third estate was thus in the unenviable position of carrying a tax load almost beyond endurance.

Louis XVI accepted the idea of the three estates as a natural way of life for his country, paying scant attention to the hardships borne by the majority of his subjects. What he was very well aware of, however, was that his own coffers were empty. To remedy the situation, he had the good sense to appoint the capable economist Robert Jacques Turgot as minister of finance early in 1775.

In analyzing the reasons for the country's financial straits Turgot became aware of the great drain on the treasury due to the purchase of gunpowder. Here, just as the collection of taxes was leased to the Farmers-General, so was the supplying of gunpowder leased out to a group of financiers. These men were supposedly obligated to furnish a million pounds of gunpowder a year to the government at a fixed rate. But, if they happened to fall short of their obligation one year, they did not have to make up the amount the following year. Therefore, since they enjoyed a monopoly in its manufacture, they were reaping a handsome profit selling powder elsewhere at higher rates. Thus the government, finding itself short of ammunition, was being forced to buy gunpowder from other countries at exorbitant prices.

The corrupt practices of the gunpowder manufacturers led Turgot to seek a means of breaking their monopoly. In doing so, he needed a thorough study to be made of both the chemistry involved in the manufacture of the explosive and an efficient way of financing its production. One man stood out above all the others in possessing the necessary qualifications for this study—the chemist and Farmer-General Antoine Lavoisier. Accordingly, Turgot asked Lavoisier to look into the whole business and submit a report as soon as possible.

Lavoisier's report to Turgot suggested a number of changes, and the minister took careful note of them. First and foremost, Turgot bought out the contract of the gunpowder manufacturers together with their plants and materials on hand. Next he established a Gunpowder Commission—the *Régie des Poudres*—composed of four commissioners who would be responsible to the minister of finance. The commissioners were to be paid for their work and a bonus given them as the production of gunpowder increased.

As both a chemist and a competent financier Lavoisier was asked to become one of the four gunpowder commissioners on June 30, 1775. In addition to his salary the position carried with it the use of a house and laboratory in the Paris Arsenal.

Early in July Marie and Antoine Lavoisier moved from their home in the rue Neuve des Bons-Enfants to the Arsenal. Aunt Constance went with them to their new home. The mutual love and respect of the now middle-aged Mlle. Constance Punctis and her nephew and niece-by-marriage had not diminished in these years. Gladly she once more took over the reins of the household, leaving Marie to pursue her own interests.

That summer of 1775 Lavoisier devoted most of his time to the Gunpowder Commission, working with the other commissioners to organize the new government agency as an efficiently run operation. Necessarily, he neglected his own scientific work, although he made good progress in setting up his laboratory in the Arsenal. He looked forward to many years of fruitful work in it, both for himself and for the government of France.

In autumn of that year, just as the Lavoisiers had become settled in their routine at the Arsenal home, Antoine suffered a severe personal loss. His father, while at his summer home at Le Bourget near Paris, died suddenly of a stroke. When the news was broken to him Antoine rushed to Le Bourget, but there was little he could do except make funeral arrangements. That he had not been present at his father's last moments added greatly to his grief. Rarely had a father and his son been so close. In writing of his father's death, Antoine said, "It is less the loss of a father that I mourn, than the loss of my best friend."

Sadly, Lavoisier turned back to his work for the Gunpowder Commission. Under his leadership the Commission, within ten months, began to show a profit for the government. And in less than a year it was even possible to export a good grade of gunpowder to other countries.

A most eager customer for this product was the Continental Congress of the British colonies in America, which were then in rebellion against England. These thirteen colonies on July 4, 1776, had declared their independence of England. But England had refused to recognize this declaration, and King George III had sent troops to America to quell the revolt. The American Revolutionary War was at its height, and the colonists were now badly in need of ammunition to pursue it. In desperation, they turned to France, believing that country would gladly sell them some at a fair price.

The colonists knew that for many years France and England had been enemies, sometimes to the point of open warfare. Only thirteen years before France had suffered a severe military defeat at the hands of the English in the Seven Years' War, known in America as the French and Indian War. At the peace treaty of 1763, which ended that conflict, France was forced to cede all of her possessions in North America to England. Ever since that time France had always welcomed any opportunity to weaken or embarrass England, short of war. And now, selling gunpowder to Britain's American colonies was such an opportunity.

The Continental Congress, needing a representative in Paris to negotiate for the purchase, voted to send Benjamin Franklin on this delicate mission. In addition to Franklin's diplomatic talents another reason for sending him was the good relations he had established through correspondence with a very influential member of the Gunpowder Commission, Antoine Lavoisier.

Franklin reached Paris in December of 1776. One of the first steps he took to fulfil his mission was to ask to see Lavoisier. Among other things, as a scientist himself he wanted to discuss with the Frenchman methods of improving the quality of gunpowder. Marie, at first as a duty, invited the American to dinner. As did her husband, she enjoyed Franklin's company so much that he became a frequent visitor and friend of the Lavoisiers. Both the American colonies and the Lavoisiers were to profit immensely by this friendship,—the former in a material way, the latter by the warmth of a great friendship.

"EMINENTLY RESPIRABLE AIR" IS
RENAMED "OXYGEN"

TWELVE

THE LAVOISIERS' HOUSE in the Arsenal soon became the gathering place for many of the most eminent men in France. Among the guests were such great names as Jean Jacques Rousseau, the philosopher; Jean Antoine Condorcet and Pierre-Simon Laplace, the mathematicians; Denis Diderot, the chief editor of the French Encyclopedia; the chemist Claude Louis Berthollet, and Benjamin Franklin. Visiting scientists of all nations were also received with great courtesy. The conversation ranged from art, music, the theater, philosophy and politics, to science.

Adjoining the Lavoisiers' living quarters was the laboratory. While the Gunpowder Commission had furnished some of its equipment, most of it was bought by Lavoisier himself at his own expense. He considered the best none too good for the laboratory. And his personal wealth made it possible to employ the most skilled glassblowers and instrument makers in the country to make every conceivable piece of scientific apparatus. Before long the laboratory became known as the finest in France.

Experiments were always being performed there, either by Lavoisier himself or by other chemists who were invited to do so. Lavoisier was especially generous in permitting the use of the laboratory to poor young men studying science. He wanted these eager students to reap some of the benefits of his own good fortune in having been born to wealth.

Ever since he had joined the Farmers-General and the Academy, of which he was now a full member, Lavoisier had never been able to refuse a request that he serve on this or that committee. Often he was asked to act as its secretary and to submit its report. The Gunpowder Commission, too, was making demands on his time. He soon saw that he would have to set himself a rigid schedule if he were to finish all of the work required of him.

Only the unfailing good health he enjoyed all of his life permitted him to carry on as strenuous a program as he did. From six o'clock to nine in the morning, and from seven to ten in the evening he spent in his laboratory. The rest of the day except for mealtimes he worked at many other duties that had fallen upon him. One whole day a week, however, he spent in the laboratory on experimental work. That day, he said, he considered his holiday from work.

Again and again, using his delicate and precise instruments, Lavoisier repeated his tests with mercury calx, sulphur, phosphorus, lead, and tin. While he discovered

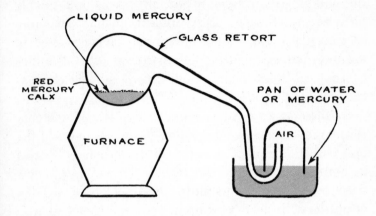

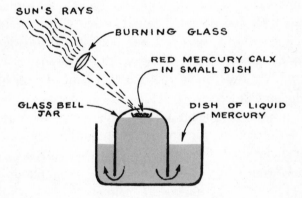

Above: When the liquid mercury was heated in air, drops of a red powder, mercury calx, appeared on top of the liquid mercury in the retort.

Below: When mercury calx was heated, "eminently respirable air" was given off, and liquid mercury was left in the dish.

nothing of any importance that was new, he was neverthe-less confirming his theory about combustion and calcina-tion and the part "eminently pure air" played in it. Finally he conducted a series of experiments that satisfied him that not the *whole* air but only a part of it was used in burning and calcination. This part was what Priestley called "dephlogisticated air" and what he himself chose to call "eminently respirable air."

In these experiments he first heated liquid mercury gently in a confined volume of air for twelve days. At the end of that time about one-sixth of the air had been used up and some red calx of mercury was formed. (We know today, with our more precise means of measurement, that one-fifth of the air is used up in this experiment.) Lavoi-sier tested the remaining five-sixths of the air and found that it extinguished a flame and asphyxiated a mouse. He then heated the mercury calx to a high temperature in an-other flask and obtained liquid mercury again, plus the same amount of "air" that had been used up in forming the calx. Upon mixing this gas with the "asphyxiating air" of the first experiment, he discovered that he once more had common air.

Lavoisier had shown in these experiments that the calci-nation of mercury is a reversible reaction; that is,

mercury + "eminently respirable air = mercury calx

mercury calx — same amount of "respirable air"

as above = mercury

Today, we would write the chemical reaction this way:

mercury + oxygen ⇌ mercuric oxide

Phlogiston was in no way involved in these reactions. In fact, Lavoisier was now sure it did not exist. Moreover, he had shown that common air was not *one* gas, part of which was "eminently respirable." Instead, it consisted of at least *two* gases, one of which supported respiration and combustion, the other of which did not. He called this second gas "mofette," and later "azote"—both meaning "asphyxiating air." It is the gas we now call nitrogen. The first gas, oxygen, he still called "eminently respirable air."

The last of this series of experiments was with the air breathed out by animals. Lavoisier found, as had Joseph Black before him, that air breathed out contained, in addition to "fixed air" or carbon dioxide, as much of the "mofette" as breathed in. He reasoned, therefore, that the "mofette" entered and left the lungs unchanged, and that the "respirable air" was changed to "fixed air". He thought too that the body probably used this "respirable air" to furnish heat and that the "air" combined with the blood in some way he did not understand, to give it its red color.

All of these experiments Lavoisier repeated in his laboratory in the presence of his fellow-chemists of the Academy, and also for any foreign scientists who happened to be in Paris. This was a procedure Lavoisier had established early in his scientific career, possibly as a precaution against charges of deception which might later be leveled at him.

At last Lavoisier felt that he was ready to launch an open attack on the phlogiston theory. On the bright spring afternoon of May 3, 1777, he stood before the Academy and began to read a paper on his experiments. After he had been reading the paper for some minutes, in his clear, precise manner, Lavoisier noticed that the audience had become even more attentive than usual. He could see the members were trying to make certain that they understood what his latest experiments proved. He fancied they were

asking themselves if in effect he was telling them that phlogiston was nothing more than a figment of their imaginations. Indeed, how else could they possibly interpret his
conclusions?

When Lavoisier finished his report he saw he had provoked considerable discussion among the Academy members, and a great deal of scepticism as well. Many of the
older Academicians had been brought up on what appeared to be a workable theory of burning. These men
were not yet ready to change a lifetime of thinking because
of the experiments of a thirty-four-year-old "youth."
Others however were willing, even eager, to learn more
about Lavoisier's theory. Lavoisier knew then that he had
better follow whatever advantage he had and hammer
away, over and over again, at his new theory of combustion.

With this purpose in mind, he read another paper before
the Academy a week later. In this one he spoke mainly of
his experiments on the calcination of lead and tin in closed
vessels, without the possibility of phlogiston either entering or leaving. Again he emphasized that common air was
not just one gas, but was made up of "eminently respirable
air" needed for calcination and the asphyxiant "mofette."

Altogether, in the year 1777, Lavoisier read nine papers
on combustion before the Academy, always pounding away
at the same theme. While there was not much that was
new in these memoranda, Lavoisier hoped they might
stimulate enough discussion to gain more converts to his
theory.

Abroad, particularly in England, scientists were taking
careful note of Lavoisier's work. Yet Joseph Priestley, the
one man whom the French chemist wanted most to con-
vince of the correctness of his interpretation of burning,

remained adamant. Not that Priestley was unaware of Lavoisier's experiments. On the contrary, he was corresponding regularly with Benjamin Franklin and learning from him as well as from other sources of the scientific developments in France. Franklin made no secret of this correspondence with Priestley, since the friendship between the two men was well known. Still, not even when Priestley read first-hand accounts from Franklin of some of Lavoisier's experiments would he change his ideas. Nor, strange as it may seem, did Franklin himself ever commit himself one way or the other to Lavoisier's new theory of burning.

The only important memorandum Lavoisier read before the Academy in 1778 concerned burning and "fixed air." In it, he repeated the familiar fact that the calx of a metal when heated with charcoal gave the pure metal and "fixed air," while the charcoal disappeared. Charcoal, he stated, was known to be carbon and the gas released from the calx was "eminently pure air." It followed then that the charcoal disappeared as it combined with the air given off by the calx to make "fixed air." The "fixed air" that Joseph Black had discovered in 1756 was therefore nothing more than carbon plus "eminently pure air." We would now say that carbon dioxide gas is composed of carbon plus oxygen. This paper was added to the others Lavoisier had written on calcination and combustion, and later published in the *Memoires* of the Academy.

For three full months in that year of 1778 Lavoisier had to abandon all other work to travel into the provinces prospecting for saltpeter for the Gunpowder Commission. This trip took him deeper into the farm lands of France than he had been for some time—and closer to the farmer. He talked with them about their methods of cultivating the fields, raising crops, and caring for their cattle. In this manner Lavoisier learned of the problems of the farmer, and, as a scientist, he thought there must be some solution to many of these problems. He therefore began to cast about in his mind for ways of improving methods of agriculture and raising livestock. And again, as a scientist, he could expect to find these ways only by experimenting.

However, Lavoisier could not experiment in agricultural methods in the Arsenal laboratory. And so, as he traveled about, he kept his eyes open for a piece of land that he might purchase for use as an experimental farm. Several prospects presented themselves, and after his return to Paris he bought the chateau and estate of Freschines near Blois, about a hundred miles southwest of Paris. Subsequently, Freschines became both a country home for the Lavoisiers and one of the first experimental farms in Europe.

But before he did any significant work at the farm Lavoisier attended to one matter that had been on his mind for some time. "Eminently respirable air" was an awkward name for a gas as important as the one he was sure was needed for combustion. And, in his opinion, the term "dephlogisticated air" was even worse because it was obviously incorrect. The name this gas should bear, Lavoisier decided, must be both simple and descriptive of its properties. When burned, those chemicals he had used in his combustion experiments, mainly sulphur, phosphorus, and carbon, gave off a product which dissolved in water and formed an acid. Nitric acid, too, could be shown to contain this gas. What better name, for it then, than a word meaning "acid-maker?"

On November 23, 1779, Lavoisier read a paper before the Academy in which for the first time he called his "eminently respirable air" *oxygen*. He explained that he had coined the word from two Greek words meaning "acid" and "I make." Actually he was unaware that some acids do not contain oxygen. In fact, a common one, hydrochloric acid, is made up of hydrogen and chlorine, and another less common one, hydrofluoric acid, of fluorine and hydrogen.

Nevertheless "oxygen" remained the name for the gas that combines with metals in calcination and with fuels in combustion. We still call it by the name Lavoisier gave it in 1779.

THE REVOLUTION IN CHEMISTRY IS
LAUNCHED

THIRTEEN

Across the Atlantic the tide of the American Revolutionary War had turned against England. With the surrender of General Burgoyne at Saratoga in 1777 it seemed possible that the thirteen colonies would at last gain their independence. Still, in spite of their successes, the colonies were badly in need of ammunition and money to continue fighting. Benjamin Franklin already had been able to purchase saltpeter for them from the Gunpowder Commission, and to send two powder-makers to America to instruct the colonists in that craft. His friendship with Lavoisier had undoubtedly been of great help in achieving this. Now the Continental Congress sought to obtain a loan from France to continue the war. Franklin remained in Paris as head of a commission to try to secure it.

When approached for this loan, the French government found itself in a quandary. On the one hand its own treasury was very low, largely because of Queen Marie Antoinette's thoughtless extravagances. The finance minister Turgot, who had sought to curb the Queen's spending, had been dismissed after a year, mainly at the insistence of the Queen and her dissolute friends. Nor had Turgot's successor Jacques Necker been able to put the government finances on a firm footing. In short, France was in no position to lend money to anyone.

Yet on the other hand the king knew that, should England crush the revolt of her American colonies, Britain's wealth and power would undoubtedy increase. In time Britain might even find a pretext to invade France herself. Benjamin Franklin, shrewd politician and diplomat that he was, played upon these fears of King Louis XVI and on his great desire to weaken England. Thus, to the benefit of the American colonies but to the detriment of the fortunes of the king, in 1778 France loaned a large sum of money to the Continental Congress. The commission headed by Franklin, having achieved its purpose, was then dissolved. The other members sailed for home, but Franklin remained in Paris as official ambassador to the French court.

His main mission on behalf of the Continental Congress now accomplished, Franklin became a more frequent guest at the Lavoisier home. He worked with the chemist on several projects concerning gunpowder and, it is believed, helped him prepare some of the reports for the Academy. And Marie, who with proper instruction in art had discovered she possessed even more talent than she at first knew, considered painting a portrait of the elderly American as a token of her affection. Lately she had begun to study painting under the great artist Jacques Louis David, and hoped soon to become proficient enough to paint Franklin's portrait.

Meanwhile, Lavoisier had begun his agricultural experiments at Freschines. The work went slowly for many reasons. For one thing, he himself knew very little about farming, nor was he able to learn much from the neighboring farmers. Besides, it took a whole growing season to find the results of an experiment. But discouragement was not a word in Lavoisier's vocabulary. Every spring and autumn he spent several weeks at Freschines, always learning, trying new ideas, and making careful records of what he had done. All the farm records were made in duplicate, one set to remain at the farm and the other for study in Paris.

The more efficient Lavoisier's investigations into matters other than chemistry proved to be, the more demands were made of him. One of these, made by the Academy at the request of the Finance Minister Necker, was to serve on a committee to investigate the prisons of Paris.

Lavoisier and the other committee members were appalled at what they found in these institutions. The filth and neglect were unbelievable, as was the brutal treatment of the prisoners. The ensuing report, written in Lavoisier's handwriting, made a number of suggestions for reforms. Running throughout the report were statements showing that the committee considered the prisoners were men, not beasts, and should be afforded the dignity due them as human beings. They should, moreover, be treated so that they might resume their place in society when they were released.

Further, the report called for the tearing down of the pestilential old prisons from which a prisoner, when released, could carry disease to his home. Plans were suggested for the construction of new prisons having proper ventilation and adequate water supply and sewage systems. This *memoire* on prison reform was submitted to the Academy in 1780. By 1783, most of the old prisons were replaced by new ones in keeping with the recommendations of the committee.

These were busy, fruitful, and happy years for Marie and Antoine Lavoisier. Their only sadness lay in the fact that they had no children of their own to love, who might carry on their name and inherit their fortune. In January of 1781 they were further saddened by the death of Aunt Constance. For thirty-three years she had been as a mother, first to Antoine and later to Marie as well. Indeed, it was more as a mother that the Lavoisiers mourned Mlle. Punctis than as an aunt. In a letter Lavoisier wrote to Franklin shortly after her death, he asked the American's forgiveness for being remiss in not speeding onward a shipment of saltpeter. He wrote:

"The excuse I have to offer you, is of such a nature as to merit all your indulgence. I have just had the misfortune of losing an aunt, who has always been a second mother to me, and to whom I could not be more tenderly attached. This sad event has absorbed me entirely, and has caused me to neglect many of my duties."

But great as Lavoisier's grief was, he could not remain idle for long. The Academy, the Farmers-General, the Gunpowder Commission, and now the experimental farm at Freschines, all kept him busier than he may have wished to be. Lately, he had done nothing of particular interest in his laboratory, so taken up was he with administrative duties. However, in 1782, together with the mathematician Pierre Simon Laplace, he began a new series of experiments on respiration and its relation to combustion.

In his report on combustion in 1777 Lavoisier had said that the "air" which by 1782 he was calling oxygen was changed to "fixed air" in the lungs. During this process, he had said, heat was given off just as when charcoal burned to give "fixed air." He had added that he believed this to be the means by which an animal's body produces its heat or, as he called it, "caloric." Now, five years later, he returned to his experiments on respiration to prove this once and for all.

To show that the body heat resulted from this change in oxygen, Lavoisier thought it necessary to measure two factors. The first was the amount of oxygen an animal breathed in a known period of time. The second was the amount of heat—or "caloric"—an animal's body had to produce to keep its temperature constant in that same time. Lavoisier and Laplace had no difficulty measuring the amount of oxygen given an animal, but measuring the amount of heat produced presented a problem. Such an experiment had never been done before, and the two scientists had to find a method of their own. They therefore developed an "ice calorimeter," a most ingenious device to measure heat given off in any chemical process. With some slight changes, the ice calorimeter is used in laboratories for this purpose to this day.

The principle of the ice calorimeter was based on work done by Joseph Black in 1761. Black had remarked that all the ice in a bucket did not instantaneously melt when heat was applied to it. Therefore it must slowly take in large quantities of heat in order to effect this change. Black called the heat absorbed by the ice "latent heat," meaning hidden heat, because it could not be measured by a thermometer. He had even calculated that a piece of ice needed 80 percent as much heat to melt as it took to raise an equal weight of water from its freezing point to its boiling point.

Lavoisier and Laplace were familiar with Black's calculations, and decided to use them in their own work. To do so, they first divided a large bucket into three round compartments, one inside the other. The innermost compartment was for charcoal or some other fuel, or for a live animal. The middle one was filled with a weighed amount of ice, and the outside one packed with snow to insulate the ice from the heat of the air. Obviously, the ice calorimeter as used by Lavoisier and Laplace could function only in the winter.

When a fuel was burned in the innermost compartment, the heat it provided melted some of the ice. Knowing how much "caloric" was needed to melt a given amount of ice, it was a simple matter to measure how much ice had melted, and thus calculate the heat released by the burning fuel. The heat given off by the body of a small animal such as a guinea pig could also be measured in this way, by placing the animal inside the calorimeter.

The scientists knew that the body of a warm-blooded animal remained at constant temperature, even when it gave off some heat to its surroundings. Lavoisier and Laplace wanted to know how much heat an animal needed to produce to keep its own temperature constant while losing heat to its environment.

They started by placing a guinea pig in the calorimeter for ten hours, and measuring the amount of heat its body

Left: The ice calorimeter developed by Lavoisier and Laplace.
Right: The ice calorimeter cut away to show the three compartments.

released to the ice. Then, by burning weighed pieces of charcoal, collecting and weighing the "fixed air" yielded, and calculating the amount of heat given off, they knew how much heat was released in the production of any amount of "fixed air." Lastly, they determined how much oxygen was breathed in and how much "fixed air" was breathed out by the guinea pig in ten hours, the same period of time it had spent in the ice calorimeter.

In this way Lavoisier and Laplace could calculate the amount of heat produced in the body of the guinea pig in those ten hours. It proved to be the same amount the animal lost to the ice in those same hours. Therefore, the body of the little animal was making enough heat to offset any loss to its surroundings, and so was able to keep its temperature constant. The two scientists finally concluded that "respiration is therefore a combustion, admittedly very slow, but otherwise similar to that of charcoal . . . the heat developed in this combustion is communicated to the blood which passes through the lungs and thence diffuses through the whole animal system."

Although they did not know it, the two scientists in these experiments were the first to measure in a crude way "basal metabolism," the rate at which the body burns food to maintain its life processes.

At the same time that these experiments on respiration were being conducted, Lavoisier undertook another ambitious project. Since 1772, when he had first begun to question the existence of phlogiston, he had experimented and written a great deal on a different theory to account for burning and calcination. Now he proposed to summarize and interpret all of his work in a single memorandum—one so strongly worded as to deal the phlogiston theory its deathblow. The summary, which he called *Réflexions sur Phlogistique—Reflections on Phlogiston*—was submitted to the Academy in 1783.

Lavoisier's book was a masterly piece of writing. First, he insisted, all previous notions must be put aside. Chemists, for the moment, must consider themselves as living in the days before Stahl, and must forget that the phlogiston theory had ever been devised. Lavoisier next gave a historical account of all that had been done to make the phlogiston theory fit the observed facts, and of the ways chemists found to explain away contradictions that continually came up. He wrote:

"Chemists have turned phlogiston into a vague principle which consequently adapts itself to all the explanations for which it may be required. Sometimes the principle has weight, and sometimes it has not; sometimes it is free fire and sometimes it is fire combined with the earthly element; sometimes it passes through the pores of vessels, sometimes these are impervious to it . . . It is a veritable Proteus, changing in form at each instant."

Finally, and most important of all, Lavoisier proposed that all chemists adopt his own theory of combustion as basic to the proper understanding of chemical facts. He then proceeded to summarize briefly his theory as proposed before the Academy in 1777. He concluded with these words: . . . "all the facts of combustion and calcination are explained in a much simpler and much easier way without phlogiston than with it. I do not expect that my ideas will be adopted at once; the human mind inclines to one way of thinking and those who have looked at Nature from a certain point of view during a part of their lives adopt new ideas only with difficulty; it is for time, there-

RÉFLEXIONS
SUR LE PHLOGISTIQUE,

Pour servir de développement à la théorie de la Combustion & de la Calcination, publiée en 1777.

Par M. LAVOISIER.

DANS la suite de Mémoires que je viens de communiquer à l'Académie *, j'ai passé en revue les principaux phénomènes de la Chimie; j'ai insisté sur ceux qui accompagnent la combustion, la calcination des métaux, & en général toutes les opérations où il y a absorbtion & fixation d'air. J'ai déduit toutes les explications d'un principe simple, c'est que l'air pur, l'air vital, est composé d'un principe particulier qui lui est propre, qui en forme la base, & que j'ai nommé *principe oxygine*, combiné avec la matière du feu & de la chaleur. Ce principe une fois admis, les principales difficultés de la Chimie ont paru s'évanouir & se dissiper, & tous les phénomènes se sont expliqués avec une étonnante simplicité.

Mais si tout s'explique en Chimie d'une manière satisfaisante, sans le secours du phlogistique, il est par cela seul infiniment probable que ce principe n'existe pas; que c'est un être hypothétique, une supposition gratuite: & en effet, il est dans les principes d'une bonne logique, de ne point multiplier les êtres sans nécessité. Peut-être aurois-je pu m'en tenir à ces preuves négatives, & me contenter d'avoir prouvé qu'on rend mieux compte des phénomènes sans phlogistique qu'avec le phlogistique: mais il est temps que je m'explique d'une manière plus précise & plus formelle sur une opinion

---

* Quelques-uns de ces Mémoires ne sont point encore imprimés.
Mém. 1783. Sſſ

fore, to confirm or reject the opinions I have advanced. Meanwhile, I see with much satisfaction that young men, who are beginning to study the science without prejudice, geometers and physicists, who bring fresh minds to bear on chemical facts, no longer believe in phlogiston . . ."

Thus, with the publication of his *Réflexions sur Phlogistique* Lavoisier succeeded in tearing the phlogiston theory to shreds and launched the revolution in chemistry.

LAVOISIER'S MANY TALENTS ARE PUT
TO USE

FOURTEEN

THERE SEEMED TO BE no end to the commissions on which Antoine Lavoisier was asked by the Academy to serve. These constantly took him away from his own laboratory work and from experiments with which he hoped to gain full acceptance for his theory of combustion. Yet the very fact that his own interests covered so wide a range made him the logical person for these appointments, and he accepted them willingly.

One such commission was set up to investigate balloon flights and to make recommendations for further investigations in that field. Lavoisier, as usual, was chosen to submit the commission's report. This particular investigation was prompted by the success of the Montgolfier brothers in sending up a balloon filled with hot air. The two brothers had done this by using as their craft a large bag of cloth and paper partly inflated with air, and open at the bottom. Attached to the opening was a basket in which straw was set on fire. As the fire heated the air in the bag, the air expanded and inflated the balloon. Since the hot air was lighter than the colder surrounding air, it caused the balloon to rise. The lighter-than-air craft traveled more than a mile before the fire died out, the air inside the bag cooled, and the balloon drifted slowly to the ground.

With the help and supervision of the commission, the Montgolfier brothers carried on several other experiments with balloons. They also tried to make them larger and capable of carrying a load in a second basket. In one of these experiments, performed before the royal court at Versailles in September of 1783, a balloon carrying a sheep, a cock, and a duck remained aloft for ten minutes before floating gently down to the ground. The animals, the first air-borne passengers in history, were unharmed by their trip.

More information about this novel way of travel was needed. Could human beings survive such an ascent? The commission encouraged Pilâtre de Rozier, a balloon enthusiast, to find out. His first attempt, made in a captive balloon anchored by ropes, carried him safely a hundred feet into the air. After more experimentation, on November 21, 1783, de Rozier and the Marquis d'Arlandes made a daring ascent in a free-floating balloon. They remained in the air about seventeen minutes and traveled about five miles before descending safely. Thus, with the aid of the commission of which Lavoisier was a most important member, the first manned aircraft made a sucessful flight.

While these investigations with hot-air balloons were

Man's first flight, which took place in Paris in 1783. Pilâtre de Rozier and the Marquis d'Arlandes rose from the ground in a Montgolfier balloon that had been inflated with hot air.

being conducted, the French scientist J. A. C. Charles successfully constructed a balloon filled with "inflammable air,"—hydrogen—, which was known to be lighter than common air. Together with a friend he made a safe flight in this craft on December 1 of that same year. A question now arose—which was more efficient, a balloon filled with hot air, or one with "inflammable air?"

When the commission finally submitted its report in January of 1784, certain aspects of balloon flight were recommended for further investigation. The first of these was the use of a light but strong material for the body of the balloon. Second, since the gas used to inflate the bag had to be light and easily produced, the use of "inflammable air" was suggested as superior to hot air. Finally, the report recommended that a means of steering be found, and a way to ascend and descend at will without loss of gas.

No sooner had this report been submitted and the commission dissolved, than Lavoisier was appointed to another one whose task was to study so-called "animal magnetism" as a method of curing disease. This method, invented by the Austrian physician Friedrich Anton Mesmer, had also come to be called "mesmerism." Those who practised it claimed that by "animal magnetism" they could spread their own good health to the sick.

This transfer, mesmerists said, was made by having the sick person hold an iron rod at the part of the body affected, while the "doctor" made mystical passes with another iron-encrusted rod. Sometimes they claimed it was necessary to touch the person to affect a cure. As the "animal magnetism" entered the body of the patient a "crisis" occurred during which the sick person often appeared to be hysterical. Then, as the hysteria passed and the patient quieted down, the cure was supposed to be effected.

In Paris, Dr. Charles Deslon, a disciple of Mesmer, had been practising "mesmerism" for several years. Many reputable physicians claimed Dr. Deslon was a fraud; to decide the matter the king asked the Academy to investigate "mesmerism." The commission appointed to do this was made up of both physicians and scientists. Among them was Benjamin Franklin, whose curiosity and doubts about the process were well known. And once more, Lavoisier was to write the report.

Dr. Deslon, confident of the soundness of his treatment, offered the commission as much help as it asked for, and even permitted the investigators to watch him at work. The first thing the members noticed was that most of the patients were women who were, they believed, more easily susceptible to suggestion and hysteria than men. Nor could the scientists find any sign of "animal magnetism" by any test known to them. Then, to prove that such "animal magnetism" did not exist, the members of the commission used Dr. Deslon's technique and apparatus on each other and felt no effects whatsoever.

Other tests were conducted by the commission on patients who were blindfolded and told they were being "magnetized." In actual fact nothing was being done to them although frequently these people reported themselves reaching a "crisis." The same persons, still blindfolded, were then "magnetized" but were not aware that they were being treated. When this was done no "crisis" occurred.

Ultimately the commission's report, written by Lavoisier in August of 1784, stated that "animal magnetism" was nothing more than a hoax perpetrated upon the gullible.

Any reported "cures" had been made on patients who were not very ill to begin with and whose imaginations led them to feel well again. As a result the practice of mesmerism in Paris was forbidden.

In addition to serving on these two commissions, Lavoisier continued to plan the work on his experimental farm at Freschines and to note down the results. He had already succeeded in proving to the farmers that rotation of crops gave a better yield. He also demonstrated that a field permitted to lie fallow one year for grazing purposes became more fertile the following season. Another innovation he advocated was the fencing in of cattle and sheep, rather than letting the animals roam at will. In this way the manure produced by the animals might be collected and used as a most effective natural fertilizer. By this time, six years after he had first started them, Lavoisier's agricultural experiments at his estate were bringing prosperity to the farmers who followed his suggestions. Many who had at first resisted any change in their methods had now begun to realize that the scientist could teach them something about farming.

During these years, Lavoisier appeared never to tire in his efforts to explore every aspect of science, be it the flight of balloons, alleged medical "cures," or agricultural techniques. And yet, in spite of all of these tasks performed in 1783 and 1784, part of his mind and energies were taken up with his own scientific experiments. These he could never give up.

"WATER IS NOT AN ELEMENT"

FIFTEEN

⚜ T RUE TO Antoine Lavoisier's expectations the older and more established chemists had not readily accepted his anti-phlogiston chemistry. Only the younger mathematicians and physicists who knew little about chemistry to begin with could see the logic of Lavoisier's new theory of combustion. The old idea that the world was made of the four elements of earth, air, fire, and water was slow in dying.

Then too, one single unanswered question kept chemists from flocking to Lavoisier's standard. The answer to this question puzzled Lavoisier, too. What happened to "inflammable air" when it burned in common air, or even in oxygen? If the new theory of combustion was correct, the oxygen should combine with the "inflammable air" to make a new substance. Upon burning, however, this gas disappeared completely. Some chemists, Joseph Priestley among them, had noticed a few drops of "dew" left in the vessel in which "inflammable air" burned, but had paid little attention to it.

In 1781 Priestley had been doing some experiments in which, by means of an electric spark, he exploded "inflammable air" in a closed vessel of ordinary air. He was not interested in any chemical change, but in whether or not heat had weight. After the explosion Priestley noticed no change in weight, but remarked on the fact that the inside of the vessel appeared "dewey." The "dew" held no significance for Priestley; it was only an observation on his part.

Priestley, wanting confirmation that there was no loss of weight in his experiment, wrote of it to Henry Cavendish, the greatest English chemist of the time. Cavendish, curious himself to find out whether heat had weight, decided to repeat Priestley's experiment. He did so, confirming the fact that there was no change in weight, and also observing the "dew." But it was the "dew," not the gain or loss of weight, that caught Cavendish's attention, and he set out to find what this "dew" was.

In his most significant experiment, Cavendish ignited a mixture of "inflammable air" and common air as each issued from a jet which led out of a vessel containing a measured quantity of that "air." Then he quickly placed a glass cylinder over the jets to collect the "dew" and tested it. Cavendish wrote, "this dew is plain water."

It never occurred to this great chemist that the "inflammable air" and the oxygen of the common air were entering into chemical combination. In fact, Cavendish remained a confirmed phlogistonist to his dying day. He explained the formation of water by saying that "inflammable air" was phlogiston itself united to water, and "dephlogisti-

cated air" was water deprived of its phlogiston. When the
two "airs" were heated together, phlogiston escaped from
the first, was seized by the second and water from each of
the "airs" was thus condensed.

In June of 1783, while Lavoisier was working on the
commission to study balloon ascents, Charles Blagden, an
assistant to Cavendish, happened to be in Paris. In speaking to Lavoisier, Blagden described in detail how the English chemist had obtained water, and that twice as much
"inflammable air" as oxygen had been needed in the
process.

Lavoisier was amazed at the news. He quickly grasped
what neither Cavendish nor Blagden had understood—
that in burning, "inflammable air" had combined with
oxygen, in the proportion of two parts "inflammable air"
to one part oxygen, to form an entirely new substance—
water. (Today we write the chemical formula for water
as H_2O). Water, therefore, was not one of the four elements of which the earth was made at all, but a compound
of "inflammable air" and oxygen. Yet Lavoisier was dis-
appointed, too, that this combination with oxygen had not
yielded an acid. Perhaps the word "oxygen" was a mis-
nomer, he thought, but he did not consider it important to
change it.

Hardly had Blagden left Lavoisier's laboratory than the
latter rushed off to consult with Laplace on ways of veri-
fying Cavendish's results. Hurriedly the two French scientists assembled suitable apparatus and on June 24, with
Blagden as a spectator, confirmed the findings of the English chemist.

The report, submitted the next day, June 25, 1783, was
quite short. Lavoisier gave few details of his experiments,

and ended by saying that together with Laplace he had burned "inflammable air" in oxygen in a closed vessel and had obtained very pure water. The report mentioned neither Cavendish's work nor Blagden's account of that English chemist's experiments.

Not until November of that year did Lavoisier read a complete memoir before the Academy of his work on water. He gave the paper a long name—*On the Nature of Water and on Experiments that Appear to Prove that this Substance is not Properly Speaking an Element, but can be Decomposed and Recombined*. The memorandum mentioned Cavendish's work casually, almost as if the English chemist had merely confirmed the findings of the Frenchman.

Upon learning of the omission of the proper credit due Cavendish, Blagden attacked Lavoisier violently. He told the scientific world of how he had described Cavendish's experiments to Lavoisier, which the Frenchman had then appropriated as his own. Dignified, highly-respected scientists took sides in the arguments that followed as to the correctness of Lavoisier's actions. The furor died down in time, but the whole matter left a blot on Lavoisier's reputation. It has generally been agreed among scientists that Lavoisier had acted unethically in not giving Cavendish credit for first discovering how water is formed. And it is also generally agreed that without Lavoisier's true interpretation of the facts, Cavendish's discovery lost much of its significance. The Englishman thought in terms of phlogiston; the Frenchman explained that water was a compound formed when "inflammable air" combined with oxygen. Thus, while Lavoisier may indeed have used Cavendish's discovery, the correct conclusion was his own.

Late in 1783 and early in 1784, Lavoisier tested this conclusion further by seeing if he could decompose water into its two gases. If he could succeed in doing so, he reasoned, no one could doubt that water was made by the combination of the two gases. The problem, however, was not as easy as it first seemed. In thinking about a way of going about it, it occurred to him that rusting is a form of calcination; if he could make the oxygen of pure water unite with iron to cause it to rust, the "inflammable air" left could be collected. He would then have further proof of the composition of water.

Lavoisier thereupon experimented with several methods of decomposing water by allowing iron to rust in a small amount of water. Each time, he was able to collect a quantity of "inflammable air." In one of his most successful experiments he used a rifle barrel filled with a known weight of small pieces of thin sheets of iron. He set the rifle barrel at a sloped angle, and heated it at the middle until it was red-hot. This was done so that water reaching that part of the tube would turn to steam. He thought steam could be decomposed more readily than liquid water. Then a weighed amount of water was slowly dropped into the upper end of the tube. The whole apparatus was so arranged that any gas escaping at the lower end would be collected, and undecomposed water passing through the tube would also be collected.

When Lavoisier and his assistants used up all of the weighed water they cooled the gun barrel and removed and weighed the iron, which had rusted in the process. The rusted iron had gained weight, and this gain plus the weight of the "inflammable air" and the undecomposed water, equalled the weight of the original water used. Here, then,

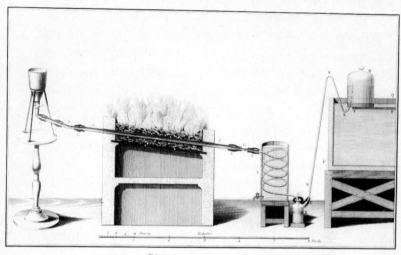

DÉCOMPOSITION DE L'EAU

Lavoisier's "gun barrel method" of decomposing water. (From Lavoisier's book Traité Élémentaire de Chimie)

was the last and final proof that water is composed of "inflammable air" and oxygen.

Lavoisier had hoped that chemists would accept his new theory of burning once he had showed that "inflammable air" burned in common air and, instead of disappearing as phlogiston, formed water. Yet one other question now arose. It still seemed logical to most chemists that "inflammable air" was phlogiston itself. Like Cavendish, they believed it escaped when a metal was dissolved in dilute acid. And, like Cavendish, they thought the "air" was not released when a calx was dissolved in acid because a metal had already lost all of its phlogiston in forming its calx.

Lavoisier offered a different explanation for this phenomenon. He maintained that in this process the "inflammable air" came not from the phlogiston-rich metal, but by the breaking down of the water of the dilute acid into its "inflammable air" and oxygen. This explanation seemed reasonable enough to overcome the objection to the new theory of combustion. If only one of the important French chemists would openly espouse his theory, Lavoisier knew his battle against phlogiston would be won.

Fortunately, such an opportunity soon presented itself as an outgrowth of the report on the flight of balloons. Following the suggestion that "inflammable air" might be better than hot air to inflate these "air-bags", Louis XVI late in 1784 asked the Academy to investigate ways of preparing large amounts of "inflammable air." The Academy appointed Lavoisier and Jean Baptiste Meusnier, another chemist, to explore methods of doing so. The two chemists decided that the easiest and cheapest way to obtain large quantities of this gas was by decomposing water. They prepared an elaboration of the gun-barrel method and suc-

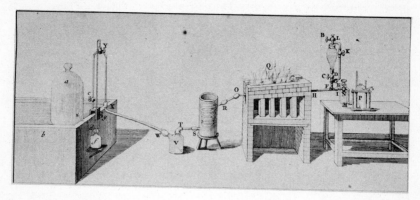

Above: Apparatus used by Lavoisier and Meusnier for the decomposition of water into its two gases.
Below: Apparatus used by Lavoisier and Meusnier for the recomposition of water from its two gases.
(From Journal Polytype, Paris, 1786. *Courtesy of Denis I. Duveen*

ceeded in freeing large quantities of "inflammable air."

With the apparatus at hand for such large-scale decomposition of water, Lavoisier conceived the idea of demonstrating that water in any amount could indeed be broken down into its two gases. By burning the "inflammable air" in the same amount of oxygen as was released, it could then be reconstituted into the original amount with but little loss.

He sought the help of Meusnier, and together they further refined and perfected their gun-barrel method of breaking down water. In addition, they devised a way of reconstituting the water, and of accurately weighing the water produced by this recombination. They planned a series of experiments to be conducted over several successive days, and asked the Academy to appoint a commission to witness these experiments.

The experiments were conducted beginning February 27, and a report on each one drawn up by one of the members of the commission. Rarely in the history of science had such an ambitious large-scale series of experiments been performed. When they were finished and the reports carefully studied, a few chemists still persisted in clinging to the phlogiston theory. But in less than two years influential chemists such as Antoine-Francois Fourcroy, Gaspard Monge, and Claude Louis Berthollet, announced their conversion to Lavoisier's anti-phlogiston theory of combustion. Their open adherence to Lavoisier's new chemistry served to sway many others, and in fact helped set the revolution in chemistry well on its way.

THE NEW CHEMISTRY GETS A NEW
LANGUAGE

SIXTEEN

❧ THROUGHOUT THESE BUSY years Marie Lavoisier worked alongside her husband as much as her time and ability permitted. The laboratory in the Arsenal became her second home. Some of the notes in the laboratory records were in her own hand, as were a number of the drawings used as illustrations. Her artistic talent had blossomed under the instruction of Jacques Louis David and now she decided to carry out her longfelt desire to paint a portrait of Franklin.

Franklin, now almost eighty years old, and ill with frequent attacks of gout, was being recalled home. As a memento of his friendship with the Lavoisiers Marie hoped to present the finished portrait to him before he sailed. But when Franklin left France on September 12,

1785 Mme. Lavoisier had not finished the painting to her satisfaction. Rather than give him an unfinished one she proposed to put the final touches to it and send it on to Philadelphia later.

Benjamin Franklin left Paris with many regrets. In the nine years he had spent in France he had grown to love the country and its people. He had made many personal friends and many others useful to his government as well. He had taken part in scientific research, in finance, and in diplomacy. When he departed the legend of a great man who had dwelt among them remained behind with the French people.

Although an ocean separated him from his American friend, Antoine Lavoisier had no intention of losing Franklin's friendship. What he was no longer able to discuss with him in person he hoped to write in letters to Franklin in Philadelphia. But unfortunately both the Farmers-General and the Academy still claimed most of his time, and so he had to neglect much of his personal correspondence.

In its capacity as official scientific advisory body to the king, the Academy was given innumerable assignments, some dull, some interesting, many of them very important. One of the latter was to investigate the biggest hospital in Paris, the Hôtel Dieu, and to recommend improvements. As so frequently happened, Lavoisier was appointed a member of the committee to carry out this assignment.

The conditions that met the eyes of the investigators in the Hôtel Dieu filled them with horror. Among other things, sanitation was non-existent, mistakes were made in administering food and medicines, patients with contagious diseases were placed among those with non-contagious diseases, and there were no stoves to supply heat. Moreover, it was a rare patient who had a bed to himself. Sometimes as many as six people lay in one bed and several others on the canopy above the bed!

The three-part report written by Lavoisier was a scathing exposé of this dreadful situation. As in his report on the prisons, the scientist's concern for the welfare of people stood out on every page. The building of four smaller hospitals to replace the crowded and filthy Hôtel Dieu was recommended. Here, too, as in the prison report, plans were included for the new hospitals, with drastic changes to be made in their construction and operation.

Upon reading the report, King Louis XVI ordered the building of the recommended new hospitals. But money was short and the plans were not carried out in France at that time. They were utilized, however, about ten years later, when the Glasgow Infirmary in Scotland was built almost entirely according to the plan Lavoisier's committee had drawn up.

About the middle of January of 1787, Louis Bernard Guyton de Morveau came from Dijon to Paris to consult with Lavoisier and others on a problem facing him. The French Encyclopedia was in the process of being compiled and de Morveau had been assigned to write the section on chemistry. It was to include all the latest chemical knowledge known at that time. The work itself was not difficult for a qualified chemist. But as de Morveau studied the names of chemicals, a hodge-podge of almost meaningless words confronted him. For example there were such terms as "salt of alembroth," "pompholix," "phagedenic water," "colcothar"—these meant nothing to anyone excepting the initiated few who had memorized each term and what it stood for.

Guyton de Morveau saw that in preparing this section of the encyclopedia he had an unparalleled opportunity to change the obscure, mystical names of chemicals into logical ones. If this were done, new and clearer nomenclature could pass more easily into the language of chemistry.

In planning such a change, he considered it better to leave the names of simple chemicals just as they were whenever feasible. Thus he retained such chemical names as sulphur, phosphorus, lead, tin, mercury, copper, and iron. Acids could well be called by their principle ingredient; therefore he suggested such names as sulphuric acid and nitric acid to replace "oil of vitriol" and "aqua fortis." The names of another large group of chemicals, the salts, might reasonably be derived from the chemicals from which they were made. Hence, "vitriol of Venus" would become copper sulphate; "martial vitriol," ferrous sulphate; and "saltpeter", potassium nitrate.

Soon after starting his work, de Morveau had written to Lavoisier and to the other chemists Berthollet and Fourcroy, describing his plan to incorporate new names into his section of the encyclopedia. He followed up his letters with a number of visits to Paris to talk to these chemists in person about his plans. The three scientists were sufficiently impressed with de Morveau's ideas to encourage him to continue making his suggested changes.

But de Morveau found himself in difficulty when he came to the section on "airs." While he himself was a phlogistonist, he was also aware that the anti-phlogiston theory was currently taking hold. According to the phlogiston theory, "inflammable air" could be called "hydro-gen," meaning "I produce water"; even "oxygen" would be acceptable. Lavoisier's name "azote" for the asphyxiat-ing part of the air was suitable, too. But, what about the calces of metals? Here were solids that were neither simple substances, salts, nor acids. Thus de Morveau very much needed the advice and opinions of other chemists, and hence his journey to Paris in January of 1787.

For nearly three months de Morveau, Berthollet, Four-croy and Lavoisier worked together to perfect a new system of naming, or a nomenclature. Most of de Morveau's pro-posals were agreed upon without any objections. All the same, the three Parisians soon saw they would have to convert de Morveau to their anti-phlogiston point of view if a proper new nomenclature were to be devised. Accord-ingly, they set out to prove to the Dijon chemist that burn-ing and calcination were really a process whereby a chem-ical combined with oxygen.

De Morveau, at first sceptical, became an ardent disciple by the end of March. The rest of the nomenclature then fell easily into place. A "calx" became an "oxide"; mercury calx became mercuric oxide; lead calx, lead oxide; rust, or calx of iron, iron oxide. "Fixed air" formed by burning car-bon became carbon dioxide because twice as much oxygen was needed as carbon to produce it. Likewise, the gas resulting when sulphur burned was given the name sulphur dioxide because, again, it was formed from one part sulphur to two parts of oxygen.

It was also obvious that different acids which formed in some cases from the same chemical contained differ-ent amounts of oxygen. To show the difference between them, the one with the greater amount of oxygen had the suffix "-ic" added to the name of its principal element, while the name of the acid with the lesser amount ended in the suffix "-ous". In this way, the two acids of sulphur became "sulphuric" and "sulphurous" acids respectively. The salts made by two such acids were also different; these became -"ates" (with more oxygen) and -"ites" (with less oxygen). Sulphates, sulphites, nitrates, nitrites, received their names according to this proposal.

In this manner, every known chemical was named. The new language of chemistry could thus become a far more useful tool for the chemist, since simply by looking at a chemical's name one had a good idea of its composition. The only remaining thing to do was to present this new system of naming before the scientific world. Lavoisier was chosen by the others to read a paper before the Academy on April 18, 1787 explaining the need for a new nomenclature; de Morveau would then present its details two weeks later.

Ten years earlier, Lavoisier recalled, he had stood in the same room in the old Louvre before the same assemblage of scientists. Some were now gone, others had been added, but the majority were still old friends and colleagues. At that time, he had been chipping away at the phlogiston theory, seeking to ring its death-knell. He remembered the questioning with which his own theory had been received at that time. This time he stood as a representative of some of the greatest chemists in France—Fourcroy, Berthollet, and de Morveau—men who had since come to his side. And knowing that Joseph Black, the most respected professor of chemistry in Britain, was now teaching his new theory of combustion gave Lavoisier added confidence as he stood before the learned members of the

Academy. No longer need he fear rejection by them.

Lavoisier began to speak of the outmoded names of chemicals and of the urgent necessity to modernize them. He said, "It is now time to rid chemistry of every kind of impediment that delays its advance; to introduce into it a true spirit of analysis; and we have sufficiently demonstrated that it is by the perfecting of its language that this reform must be brought to pass. We are doubtless very far from knowing the whole and all the parts of this science; it is therefore to be expected that a new nomenclature, although formed with all possible care, must be far from perfect; but provided that it has been undertaken upon sound principles, provided that it has been a method of naming rather than a nomenclature, it will naturally adapt itself to future discoveries; it will indicate beforehand the place and name of new substances that may be discovered, and it will need no more than particular amendment in some details."

In the course of his memorandum Lavoisier said that he and his collaborators in the new system had decided to accept Robert Boyle's definition of an element. He said, "We shall regard as simple all the substances that we cannot decompose, all that we obtain in the last resort by chemical analysis."

There was little disagreement with Lavoisier when he finished, nor later when de Morveau gave the details of the proposed change. To all appearances, the Academy members were ready to accept the new nomenclature. Still, knowing the Academy was slow in publishing reports the four chemists decided to have this one printed themselves, in order to speed the use of the new names. In

MÉTHODE

DE

NOMENCLATURE

CHIMIQUE,

Propofée par MM. DE MORVEAU, LAVOISIER, BERTHOLET, & DE FOURCROY.

ON Y A JOINT

Un nouveau Syſtême de Caractères Chimiques, adaptés à cette Nomenclature, par MM. HASSENFRATZ & ADET.

A PARIS,

Chez CUCHET, Libraire, rue & hôtel Serpente.

M. DCC. LXXXVII.

Sous le Privilége de l'Académie des Sciences.

Title page of *Méthode de Nomenclature Chimique.* (*From the Rare Books Division, New York Public Library.*)

August, 1787, the reports, with certain additions, appeared as a book called *Méthode de Nomenclature Chimique,* or *Method of Chemical Nomenclature.* The additions consisted of tables of new terms and an explanation of these tables, a comparative list of old and new names, and a dictionary of the new names. All of these were prepared by Fourcroy. The book also contained a memoir by two other chemists, Pierre Auguste Adet and Jean Henri Hassenfratz, and a report on new chemical symbols to be used in connection with the new names and new chemistry.

In less than a year, *Méthode de Nomenclature Chimique* was translated into English, and shortly thereafter into other tongues. The new chemistry had received a new language. And as Lavoisier had predicted, this is the language which, except for some slight changes, is used throughout the world today.

LAVOISIER SHOWS HIMSELF TO BE A
SOCIAL REFORMER

☙ THE THIRD ESTATE had become impatient waiting for relief from the heavy burden of taxes which it alone was forced to bear. Nor did there seem to be any such relief in sight. Provincial governors appointed by the king ruled as they chose, and since they were usually nobles their interests naturally lay with the nobility. Heedlessly they piled on the common people tax after tax, demand after demand, until the mood of the third estate became dangerously resentful.

While he was Minister of Finance, the liberal Necker had brought about some reforms by instituting a measure of democracy within each province concerning the handling its own affairs. Beginning in 1778 he had succeeded in establishing local assemblies in three provinces but he was dismissed before he could reorganize all of France. In 1787, his successor Charles Alexander Calonne decided to carry on where Necker had left off.

The Provincial Assembly of Orléans, where Freschines was situated, was orderd established in 1787. It was to consist of representatives of all three estates, some of whom were to be appointed by the king, the others to be elected by the appointees. Lavoisier, as a member of the third estate and a landowner in the province, was appointed to represent the third estate in the Assembly. The first meeting was called for September 6, 1787, and Antoine and Marie Lavoisier left Paris two days before to be in good time for the meeting.

Before leaving Paris Lavoisier took care of a small matter for a friend, Pierre Samuel duPont de Nemours. Earlier that year he had employed this friend's sixteen-year-old son as an apprentice bookkeeper. Lavoisier soon had noticed that the boy showed great interest and ability in chemistry. He therefore arranged to have the boy, Éleuthère Irénée duPont de Nemours, transferred from bookkeeping to train as a chemist.

With great pomp and ceremony, the Provincial Assembly of Orléans was opened by a representative of the king. Then plans for organizing the work of the newly-formed governmental body were laid. Because of his investigation into prison and hospital reform and experimental farming, Lavoisier was appointed to the Committee on Social Conditions and Agriculture.

At the Orléans Assembly Lavoisier showed himself to be a true liberal reformer of social ills. He advocated tax reform that would do away with some of the worst abuses of the existing system. He also proposed a type of benefit for the farmer that was very much like modern social security laws. This proposal suggested the setting up of a bank into which a person might deposit a sum regularly—one that would furnish him with an old-age annuity when he was too old to work. Provisions were made in this system for the payment of sums of money to the widows and children of depositors in this bank. Indeed, so ahead of their time were Lavoisier's proposals that had he lived in the twentieth century, he would have seen some of them operating in many countries.

Unfortunately, most of these reforms, with the exception of those concerning taxes, were not to be realized for over a hundred years. The Provincial Assembly of Orléans adjourned just before the end of 1787, and an interim committee was appointed to study the proposals made during its session. It was destined never to meet again, for political events in France were moving so rapidly that soon all provincial assemblies faded into insignificance.

The first part of the year 1788 passed quietly. As the summer came on, however, a long drought set in. The crops, so promising in the spring, withered on the stalk, and the frightening prospect of a hungry winter faced the farmers. Lavoisier, mindful of the welfare of the families in the towns of Blois and Romarantin nearest Freschines, offered to lend them money without interest. He hoped in this way, without making any demands for repayment, to tide them over the difficult period.

But in the rest of France most of the wealthy were not so thoughtful or generous. Crop failure or no, taxes still were demanded, and the grumbling of the people grew loud enough to reach the ears of King Louis XVI. Moreover, the whole financial structure of the government was in such a woeful predicament that the king became desperate in his need to find a solution to his problem. Instead of assemblies in provinces, he wanted a meeting in Paris of representatives of all of France to help untangle the sorry state of affairs.

Thus it came about that in August, 1788, King Louis issued a decree calling for a meeting of the States-General for May, 1789. This assemblage, consisting of members of all three estates, was an advisory body which met only at the king's summons. Not since 1614, during the reign of Louis XIII, had the States-General been called into session. For 175 years the kings of France had been absolute monarchs, levying taxes and making laws at their own will. Now, in dire straits, King Louis revived the institution, hoping for aid in finding a solution.

By this time Lavoisier had decided to carry out an ambitious project of his own, one that he had conceived a few years earlier. He wanted to write a textbook according to the new chemistry. It was to be simple and clear enough for a beginner to follow, and Mme. Lavoisier was to make the copperplate engravings for the illustrations. In this way, one of the earliest husband-and-wife teams in the history of science set to work to prepare *Traité Élémentaire de Chimie* or, *Elements of Chemistry* as the book was to be called. About six years previously Lavoisier had drawn up a rough outline for such a book. He used this as a guide, and began to collect and edit all the memoranda and laboratory notes of the past years to create a new, more complete outline.

The work on the book was often interrupted by the demands of his public duties. As commissioner of the Gunpowder Commission, it was Lavoisier's continual task to find better ways of making gunpowder. In performing one such task he almost lost his life. This happened during the testing of potassium chlorate at the Essonnes powder mill near Paris. The chemist Berthollet had recently discovered this new compound, and suggested its possible use as a substitute in gunpowder. An explosion while the test was being conducted killed two persons near him, yet in spite of the danger, Lavoisier was not discouraged from wanting to work with the chemical further. He wrote to the Minister of France, "permit me to beg you to assure His Majesty that my life belongs to him and to France, and that I am always ready to sacrifice it in his service when some advantage may follow, either by resuming the same work on the new powder, work which I consider necessary, or in any other way."

Late in the autumn Mme. Lavoisier received a most delightful letter from Benjamin Franklin thanking her for sending his portrait, and saying, "It is allowed by those who have seen it to have great merit as a picture in every respect; but what particularly endears it to me is the hand that drew it." He asked, too, that she thank her husband for the *Nomenclature de Chimique* he had been so good as to send him.

Near the end of that year M. and Mme. Lavoisier sat for a portrait by the greatest French painter of the time, Jacques Louis David. Although Marie Lavoisier had had her portrait painted when she was very young, this was the only one ever to be painted of Antoine-Laurent Lavoisier. The portrait of this devoted pair may be seen today at the Rockefeller Institute in New York City.

The year 1788 had now drawn to a close. The new year, 1789, was to prove to be the most momentous one in the history of France.

THE CHEMICAL REVOLUTION IS
COMPLETED . . .

EIGHTEEN

WORK ON THE *Traité Élémentaire de Chimie* proceeded rapidly, and early in 1789 the book was ready for the printer. It was divided into three parts, with a preface explaining the reasons for writing such a book at this time. These reasons were merely a repetition of what Lavoisier had said in the introduction to *Nomenclature de Chimique*. Again he stated his definition of elements by writing, ". . . by the term elements we mean to express those simple indivisible atoms of which matter is composed."

Part One of the book dealt with Lavoisier's theory concerning heat and "airs," or "elastic fluids," as the French usually called them. Lavoisier here adopted the word "gas," coined by van Helmont a century earlier, and used in 1789 by only a few other chemists. Regarding heat, Lavoi-

TRAITÉ
ÉLÉMENTAIRE
DE CHIMIE,

PRÉSENTÉ DANS UN ORDRE NOUVEAU

ET D'APRÈS LES DÉCOUVERTES MODERNES,

PAR M. LAVOISIER.

Nouvelle édition, à laquelle on a joint la Nomen-
clature Ancienne & Moderne, pour servir à l'in-
telligence des Auteurs ; différens Mémoires de
MM. Fourcroy & Morveau, & le Rapport de
MM. Baumé, Cadet, Darcet & Sage, sur la
nécessité de réformer & de perfectionner la No-
menclature Chimique.

Avec Figures & Tableaux.

TOME PREMIER.

A PARIS,

Chez CUCHET, Libraire, rue & hôtel Serpente.

M. DCC. LXXXIX.

Title page of Traité Élémentaire de Chimie. (*Courtesy New York Academy of Medicine*)

sier held a theory in common with most chemists and physicists of his time. They thought it was a material thing but without weight, to which they gave the name "caloric." In trying to explain "caloric" in his book Lavoisier wrote, "All bodies in nature are imbued, surrounded, and penetrated in every way with caloric, which fills up every interval between their particles." He believed a gas consisted of caloric plus the "base of the gas." Thus oxygen gas was oxygen base to which caloric was added, and the release of caloric produced heat when chemicals combined with it as in burning.

At the beginning of Part Two, Lavoisier gave a list of the elements, together with their new names and their corresponding old ones. He placed light and caloric at the head of the list, as "imponderable" or weightless elements, and included thirty-one of the ninety-two natural elements we know of today. The rest of this second section was devoted to the study of acids, bases, and salts.

Here, in writing about the chemical process involved in the fermentation of grapes, some very important things appeared. One was the old Arabic word "alcohol" to replace "spirit of wine" as one of the products of fermentation. Another was the use of algebraic equations to express chemical equations, thus showing a very accurate mathematical way of recording the results of an experiment. And, by using an equation, Lavoisier was then able to put into words for the first time what had been implied but never actually expressed before—the Law of Conservation of Mass. He wrote: "Nothing is created in the operations of either art or of nature, and it can be taken as an axiom that in every operation an equal quantity of matter exists both before and after the operation." In more simple mod-

	Noms nouveaux.	Noms anciens correspondans.
Subſtances ſimples qui appartiennent aux trois règnes & qu'on peut regarder comme les élémens des corps.	Lumière.........	Lumière.
	Calorique........	Chaleur. Principe de la chaleur. Fluide igné. Feu. Matière du feu & de la chaleur.
	Oxygène.........	Air déphlogiſtiqué. Air empiréal. Air vital. Baſe de l'air vital.
	Azote...........	Gaz phlogiſtiqué. Mofete. Baſe de la mofete.
	Hydrogène.	Gaz inflammable. Baſe du gaz inflammable.
Subſtances ſimples non métalliques oxidables & acidifiables.	Soufre...........	Soufre.
	Phoſphore........	Phoſphore.
	Carbone..........	Charbon pur.
	Radical muriatique.	Inconnu.
	Radical fluorique .	Inconnu.
	Radical boracique,.	Inconnu.
Subſtances ſimples métalliques oxidables & acidifiables.	Antimoine........	Antimoine.
	Argent..........	Argent.
	Arſenic..........	Arſenic.
	Biſmuth..........	Biſmuth.
	Cobolt.	Cobolt.
	Cuivre..........	Cuivre.
	Etain...........	Etain.
	Fer.	Fer.
	Manganèſe.	Manganèſe.
	Mercure.	Mercure.
	Molybdène........	Molybdène.
	Nickel..........	Nickel.
	Or.	Or.
	Platine..........	Platine.
	Plomb..........	Plomb.
	Tungſtène........	Tungſtene.
	Zinc..	Zinc.
Subſtances ſimples ſalifiables terreuſes.	Chaux..........	Terre calcaire, chaux.
	Magnéſie.........	Magnéſie, baſe du ſel d'Epſom.
	Baryte..........	Barote, terre peſante.
	Alumine.........	Argile , terre de l'alun, baſe de l'alun.
	Silice...........	Terre ſiliceuſe, terre vitrifiable.

Lavoisier's List of the Elements (1789).

ern language, we would say, "Matter is neither created nor destroyed."

Part Three of *Traité Élémentaire* was a volume by itself. It consisted of a very detailed description of the apparatus and methods used in chemistry. In fact, today we would call it a laboratory manual. Appended to this last section were a number of useful tables for quick calculations, and thirteen copper-plate engravings drawn by Marie Lavoisier.

In drawing the illustrations, Mme. Lavoisier started by first making free-hand water-color sketches of the individual pieces of apparatus. Next, she made fine-line pencil drawings of them on squared paper so that the apparatus would be drawn to proper scale; then she signed them with the name "Paulze-Lavoisier." From these drawings the figures were transferred with a fine stylus onto a copper plate, and the proper lettering added. Mme. Lavoisier set very exacting standards, nor would she accept any but perfect plates from the engraver. Then, when she finally approved a plate, she scratched the word "Bonne" meaning "good" in the lower right-hand corner, and added her initials.

The Lavoisiers, Antoine and Marie, had produced a great book. Hardly was it off the press when the first edition was sold out and another one rushed off the presses. Within a year it was translated into English by Robert Kerr and published in Edinburgh in 1790; German, Spanish, and other translations soon appeared. Lavoisier himself sent two copies to Benjamin Franklin on February 2, 1790, one for the American Philosophical Society and the other for himself. In the long accompanying letter he summarized his whole new chemistry and urged Franklin to openly support the anti-phlogiston theory. The letter ended with an account of the unhappy political situation which had by then reached the point of rebellion against the government. Lavoisier added a wish that Franklin were there in Paris to guide the people with his wisdom in those troubled times. Franklin was never able to answer Lavoisier's letter, for he died on April 17, 1790 eleven weeks after it had been sent.

With the wide acceptance of *Traité Élémentaire de Chimie* the revolution in chemistry that Lavoisier had started seventeen years earlier was complete. The new anti-

Plate VIII from Traité Élémentaire de Chimie, *drawn and engraved by Mme. Lavoisier. This is a copy of the final proof, with Mme. Lavoiser's "bonne" on it with her initials. (From the Denis I. Duveen Collection)*

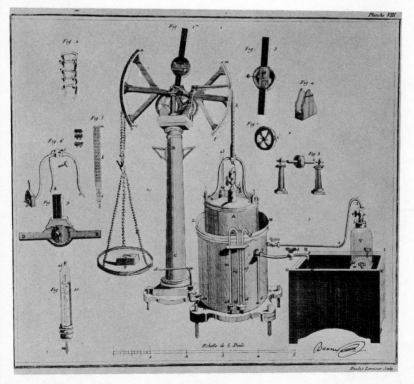

phlogiston theory was soon being taught almost exclusively wherever chemistry was taught. Yet two of England's greatest chemists, Priestley and Cavendish, remained phlogistonists to the end of their lives.

One other small group of scientists refused to accept the new chemistry. These were important only in that they published Abbé Rozier's old journal, *Observations sur la Physique*. Besides the *Mémoires* of the Academy, this was the only scientific journal of note in France. To ensure that scientific papers written in the vein of the new chemistry would be published speedily, Lavoisier, de Morveau, Berthollet, Fourcroy, and several other chemists established a new one called *Annales de Chimie*. The first issue appeared in April, 1789, and it quickly supplanted the older *Observations*. Except for the years 1793 to 1797 when publication was suspended, it has remained the most important journal of chemistry in France.

With *Traité Élémentaire* published and *Annales de Chimie* on its way, Lavoisier returned once more to the study of respiration. The first group of experiments Lavoisier conducted, with twenty-year-old Armand Séguin as assistant, were with guinea pigs. In the course of these experiments they concluded it was very probable that different amounts of oxygen were needed for breathing, depending on the activity of the animal. To verify this they boldly decided to experiment on a human being, and young Séguin offered himself as the subject.

Lavoisier had a copper mask made to fit Séguin's head snugly. The mask covered the nose and was fitted with two glass windows for the eyes. A tube entered the mask through a leather-enclosed opening near the nose to supply measured amounts of oxygen to the subject. Another tube

carried away air breathed out so that it could be collected
and analyzed.

In this manner Lavoisier was able to calculate the
amount of oxygen a healthy man needed to maintain his
body temperature with and without food, and in a warm
room or a cold room—in other words, in summer or winter.
Some of the most valuable of the experiments were those
in which they calculated the oxygen needs of a man's body
at rest and at work. In one of these, Séguin continuously
lifted a fifteen-pound weight for fifteen minutes, and the
oxygen his body used during that time was measured. In
another, Séguin was seated at a table under which a foot-
pedal had been placed. For a period of time he pressed the
pedal, and for an equal period remained at rest. Mme.

*Mme. Lavoisier's copper plate drawing of Lavoisier and Séguin con-
ducting the respiration experiments. Mme. Lavoisier is shown taking
notes. (Courtesy New York Academy of Medicine)*

Lavoisier, at a nearby table, recorded the oxygen needed by Séguin during each of these periods. In addition to acting as secretary, Mme. Lavoisier made two sketches of these last experiments showing the laboratory and its assistants, Séguin at the experimental table, and herself writing at the other.

After reading his paper on these experiments before the Academy in November, 1789, Lavoisier continued with this type of work, but it went very slowly and with constant interruptions. Indeed, it was the last work he was ever to do, for the fury of political revolution had already broken over France with the storming of the Bastille prison on July 14, 1789.

❧

. . . AS THE POLITICAL REVOLUTION
ERUPTS

❧ WHILE ANTOINE LAVOISIER's *Traité Élémentaire de Chimie* was bringing the revolution in chemistry to a successful end, the course of events in France had taken a turn leading toward political upheaval. The third estate was no longer willing to play a minor role, as it had in the past, in the States-General called for May 5, 1789. Even before this body met, it demanded a greatly increased representation, more in keeping with the number of people belonging to that estate. To satisfy the populace, Louis XVI doubled the number of seats for the third estate and thereby gave it a majority in the States-General. At the same time he issued a decree ordering elections of representatives to the May meeting.

In February of 1789, Lavoisier went to Freschines to be

present at the election of delegates for the district of Blois. There he discovered that his work at the Assembly had not been forgotten. The second estate, who considered him one of themselves, seized this opportunity to enlist his services in drawing up a list of grievances and instructions for their delegates.

The list of grievances, called the "cahier," was fair and moderate in its tone, and was adopted by the nobles at their meeting in March. Two of their number were then elected to represent them in the States-General, with Lavoisier to serve as alternate delegate. This business finished, Lavoisier returned to a Paris seething with excitement and activity in preparation for the May convocation.

In these stirring months political discussions often pushed scientific work to second place. A change was obviously imminent in France, but what kind of change became the question. Clubs of all shades of opinion were formed to debate this, and to try to influence others to accept the opinions each advanced. One of these, the "Club de 1789", counted among its four hundred members such men as the Marquis de Lafayette, the astronomer Bailly, the economist duPont de Nemours, and Lavoisier.

The "1789 Club" held a liberal, middle-of-the-road position. It wanted a constitutional monarchy for France patterned after that of England, equalization of taxes, and financial reforms within the state treasury. Some of its members, like Bailly and Lafayette, were to become important figures in the struggle to come. Lavoisier, however, still the scientist above all, contented himself with discussions rather than with intense political activity.

As the excitement mounted, delegates from all parts of France to the States-General began arriving in Paris in the spring of 1789. Nobles, clergymen, and commoners waited impatiently for the opening of the States-General at Versailles. Each hoped to contribute his share toward solving the government crisis, yet at the same time each hoped to serve the interests of the estate he represented.

Weeks of wrangling among the representatives of each estate followed the opening of the States-General. Since there was no set rule about their duties, the question arose as to which one would take the lead in forming new laws for France. Finally on June 17 the third estate, being the greatest in number, declared itself to be the legislative body and took the name National Assembly. Delegates from the other two estates were invited to join them if they so desired. The avowed purpose of the new National Assembly was to draw up a constitution for France which, among other provisions, would limit the powers of the king.

Louis XVI, alarmed at this turn of events, called out troops, hoping their presence would intimidate the members of the National Assembly. Uncertainty caused tempers to run high in the city and, to add to the difficulties, employment had become scarce in the chaotic situation. Hunger, fear, and insecurity thus urged the common people on against the only enemy they understood—the authority of the king.

In defiance of this authority, on July 14, 1789 riotous mobs broke into Les Invalides where arms were stored. They seized guns and ammunition and headed for the Bastille prison several miles away, where political prisoners were kept. On the way they were joined by armed soldiers in the city who had deserted to the people's side. Unable to withstand the onslaught of the infuriated mob, the garrison posted in the Bastille surrendered in a few hours. The revolution against the absolute power of the king of France had begun.

Fearing the danger of anarchy, the delegates from Paris to the National Assembly met at the city hall, the Hôtel de Ville. Quickly they constituted themselves the Paris Commune, the governing body for the city of Paris. Bailly was appointed Mayor, and Lafayette as head of the civil guard whose duty it was to restore order and to defend the city if necessary. On the surface at least, Paris became quiet as the authority of the Commune was recognized. Meanwhile, Paris had set an example for the rest of France. The storming of fortresses and prisons became contagious; so was the flouting of the authority of the king. In many towns and provinces the king's officials were forceably removed and communes such as the one in Paris set up. The National Assembly saw that it must take action immediately if France was to be saved from complete ruin.

Early in August, therefore, all privileges of the first and second estates were abolished and tax reforms instituted. A few weeks later, on October 2, the Assembly adopted a historic document, "The Declaration of the Rights of Man" patterned after the American Declaration of Independence.

During this spring and summer Lavoisier had been living uneasily at the Arsenal near the Bastille, not knowing from day to day if a mob might take it into its head to break into the ammunition depository. As best he could he continued his work for the Farmers-General, the Academy, and the Gunpowder Commission, with an occasional few hours for scientific work. Once the civil guard was established, he breathed easier, knowing that any disorder would be quelled quickly.

Still, Lavoisier was not entirely free from difficulties arising from his position as Gunpowder Commissioner. An incident in August made clear to him how precarious was the freedom and even the very life of a public official in such troubled days.

At that time Lavoisier had decided the Arsenal was overloaded with low-grade powder which could better be sold for export. He wanted it stored at the Essonnes plant until it could be sold and replaced with high-grade musket powder in the Arsenal. Because of a misunderstanding concerning permission to ship gunpowder out of Paris, an angry crowd gathered outside the Arsenal to shout for the arrest of Lavoisier as a traitor. To appease the mob, soldiers of the civil guard escorted him and one of the other Gunpowder Commissioners to Lafayette, commander of the ·civil guard.

All the way to the headquarters at the Hôtel de Ville the two men and their military escort were followed by the jeering, shouting mob. Whatever his own feelings may have been at receiving such shabby treatment from those he tried to serve, Lavoisier nevertheless appeared calm and composed. When he came before Lafayette, Lavoisier explained the reason for wanting to ship the poor quality powder out of the city, and was ordered released forthwith. The mob, quieted by Lafayette, then melted away. But some of the people never forgot that Lavoisier had once been accused of treason, and years later they were to use this to his detriment.

Lavoisier never spoke of this injury to his feelings brought about by this episode. He understood the desperate fear of being defenseless that had caused the people of Paris to act as they did. Nor, once the matter was settled, did either Lavoisier or the people of Paris seem to bear a grudge against the other. In fact, a month later Lavoisier was elected to the Commune of Paris and appointed member of the civil guard, now called the National Guard, in charge of the Arsenal.

Slowly the country settled down to wait for a new constitution to be written. In the emergency that faced the nation, the abilities of every man were tapped. At this point Lavoisier's talents as financier and administrator were believed to be more important to the welfare of the country than his scientific knowledge. He was therefore asked to serve on many committees, working on matters which ranged from the best way to produce paper money to the protection of gun-barrels against rust. His scientific knowledge was applied mainly in work with the Commission for Weights and Measures to set these standards for the country. Ultimately the committee was instrumental in working out the metric system still in use in most European countries and in all scientific work.

Late in 1790 the government found it needed exact information for the purpose of drawing up a budget and for passing better tax laws. Since he was known to be well informed on the economy of the country, Lavoisier was asked to draw up a survey of the potential wealth of France. Here his years of work with the Farmers-General were put to good use. He consulted his own Tax-Farm records as well as those of other members and discovered most of the needed facts were available, but scattered throughout many reports. In his precise way he organized the facts into a report which he called *The Territorial Wealth of France*. The National Assembly was so impressed with the work that it had the report printed as a source book for political economists.

Lavoisier was more than willing to cooperate with whatever government was in power if it would bring about a just solution to France's problems. But the forces set loose by the revolution began to press, sometimes unreasonably, for the abolition of the institutions of the old regime. The Gunpowder Commission came under frequent attack and the loyalty of its members, particularly Lavoisier, suspected. It appeared that the idea planted by a mob in August of 1789 in the "gunpowder incident" was not completely dead. Many pages in defense of the Gunpowder Commission were written by the Commissioners, but Lavoisier felt they sometimes were read by eyes blinded by prejudices.

From the very beginning of the revolution the Farmers-General became a prime target for attack. They were called vitriolic names such as "blood-suckers", and a cry went up for the liquidation of the Tax-Farm. Finally, on May 20, 1791, the Tax-Farm was annulled, and a committee of six of its members appointed to render an accounting to the National Assembly. Lavoisier, to his disappointment, was not asked to serve on this committee. Thus, by the stroke of a pen signing a decree, his twenty-three years of association with the Farmers-General came to an end.

In denying him a place on the committee to close the accounts of the Farmers-General, the National Assembly was not in fact overlooking Lavoisier's great talents in financial matters. Actually, these talents were more urgently needed to straighten out the affairs of the Royal Treasury, to which he was appointed a few weeks later. He accepted the appointment reluctantly, for he was still a Gunpowder Commissioner, and had no heart for further paid public office. His lettter of acceptance stated that he waived the salary offered him in this post, and wrote, "The emoluments that I enjoy as Commissioner for Gunpowder suit my way of life, my tastes, and my needs and at a time when so many good citizens are losing positions, I could not under any circumstances agree to accept a double salary."

One of his first acts as Treasury Commissioner was to ask that the name "Royal Treasury" be changed to "National Treasury." This was so ordered. Perhaps Lavoisier as well as most of France had come to see that the king would henceforth play a very small role in governing France.

Finally, after two years of deliberation, the National Assembly adopted a constitution for France. It provided for the king to remain as chief executive of the country but with sharply curtailed powers. An elected Legislative Assembly whose members must be property owners was to be the sole law-making body of the country. Although the legislators were elected, only those paying a tax equivalent to three days' work were permitted to vote.

During these days of 1791, Lavoisier had become distressed and unhappy about the turn of events in France. The middle class, or *bourgeoisie,* and the farmers were pleased with the new constitution and with what the revolution had already achieved. The privileges of the other estates had been abolished, their own tax burden had been eased, and they were enjoying a measure of prosperity. But in the cities, particularly in Paris, the working-people or, as they called themselves, the *proletariat,* were unemployed, hungry, and ragged. And, because they owned no property, none of them could sit in the legislature. Indeed, few of them could even afford to pay the tax necessary to give them the vote. They felt they had gained nothing by the revolution but the exchange of one master, the nobility, for another, the *bourgeoisie*. Led by the lawyers Danton and Robespierre, and Dr. Marat who called himself "a friend of the people", they demanded new elections to the Assembly.

The new National Assembly elected in October of 1791 turned out to be much more extreme in its thinking than the first one. As the different parties took seats according to the political positions they advocated, a sharp division soon became apparent in the assembly's ranks. The conservatives were still in favor of the absolute monarchy; liberals wanted a constitutional monarchy; and extreme reformers were in favor of a republic. Although the republicans were in the majority, they were waiting to gain more strength from the liberals before taking action.

As a moderate in favor of a limited monarchy Lavoisier was troubled by the make-up of the new Legislative Assembly. Moreover, he was sorely tired of all the demands made upon him for public service to the neglect of his scientific work. He wished it were possible to retire from public office and return to the comparative peace and security of his laboratory. His first step in that direction was to resign as Commissioner of the National Treasury in February, 1792.

Throughout these years since July 14, 1789, most of the nobility had not sat back quietly while their privileges were being taken away. Great numbers of them had liquidated whatever assets they could and fled as *émigrés* into neighboring countries. There they began a campaign to rally the nobility of the rest of Europe around them, with the cry that revolution, if unchecked in France, would spread to their own countries. These counter-revolutionary activities were centered in Prussia and in Austria, Queen Marie Antoinette's native land. Word soon reached France that armies furnished by these two countries were being sent to the borders to quell the revolution.

More than ever, the French people now felt themselves threatened by hostile forces converging on them from many sides. Defeat at the hands of these armies meant an end to their hard-won freedom. The Legislative Assembly, to counter this threat, thereupon declared war on Prussia and Austria in April, 1792. As one, the French came to the defense of their country. Citizens shouldered arms, battalions were formed all over France, and began their march to repel the invaders. In Strassbourg, a young officer, Rouget de Lisle, composed a marching song for his company from Marseilles. It quickly spread throughout France and became the song of the French army. The *Marseillaise,* is still one of the most stirring marching songs ever written and has remained the national anthem of France.

Rumors soon began to drift into Paris, however, that the French armies were suffering heavy losses and that the king and queen were revealing military secrets to the enemy. In addition, by the middle of 1792 dissension among the revolutionary parties had become rife. One group, the Jacobins, called for the complete abdication of the king and the establishment of a republic. The moderates still hoped to keep the king as nominal head of the country. Cries of "traitor" and "enemy of the state" became more frequent, even within the halls of the Academy. At last, with Georges Danton installed forceably by the mob as head of the Paris Commune, the king was suspended from office in August.

The Lavoisiers then saw that the political situation spelled danger to the *bourgeoisie,* particularly to those still connected with any of the king's commissions. They knew that they must now make a very important decision. For the sake of personal safety Antoine must resign from the Gunpowder Commission.

Thus, on August 15, 1792, Antoine Lavoisier tendered his resignation from the Gunpowder Commission, and he and his wife left the Arsenal that had been their home and laboratory for seventeen years. The magnificent laboratory, probably the finest in Europe, was dismantled, and the equipment packed and stored in the hope that it soon might be reassembled for use.

THE TERROR IS UNLEASHED

TWENTY

✥ ANTOINE AND MARIE ·LAVOISIER knew that brooding over the unhappy turn in their fortunes would be useless. Yet in their new home in the Boulevard de la Madeleine, how could they drive from their minds thoughts of the past and concern for the future? Marie at 34 and Antoine at 49 were seeing the only world they knew crumbling around them. Many of their friends were *émigrés;* others had even joined in looking for "enemies of the state."

Meanwhile, with the king no longer the head of the government, the new constitution adopted only a year earlier could not remain in effect. Therefore, to draw up a new one, a National Convention with members elected by universal suffrage was called to meet on September 21, 1792. The first act of the Convention was to abolish the monarchy and to declare France a republic. At the same time the citizens' army of the new republic was driving back the invaders who sought to restore the king to power.

It was small wonder that the Lavoisiers during their customary autumn visit to Freschines stayed at their country home longer than usual. They returned to Paris in November for the first meeting of the Academy, to find an air of gloom settled on its meeting-halls in the old Louvre. Earlier that year Fourcroy had asked the Academy to purge from its membership all *émigrés* and other members suspected of being anti-revolutionary. He argued that the Academy of Medicine had already done so, as had other learned societies.

This the Academy had refused to do on the grounds that the only qualification for membership was scientific achievement, not political 'beliefs. The National Convention did not let the matter rest there, but passed a law forbidding the appointment of new members to fill vacancies. As a result of this law, membership dwindled, and those who remained were frightened into inactivity. Because he was one of the younger men, vigorous and able, Lavoisier then found himself carrying on almost single-handed the business of the Academy. There were even times when he paid from his own pocket the salaries of those who were in need.

Despite this burden and his personal dislike of the republican government, Lavoisier tried as best he could to carry out the assignments he had undertaken for France. He was still working on the Committee on Weights and Measures and for the Commission of Arts and Crafts to which he had also been appointed. For this latter commission he was preparing a report of a committee studying ways of reforming the educational system of France.

When it was finished, the report called for free elementary education for all, with science to be taught to children from illustrated books. Different types of education in the secondary schools were recommended, depending upon whether the child was to enter a trade or a profession. The report contained such sound reasons for these changes that educators today would find them still valid.

By this time the young Republic found itself beset by problems that it had not anticipated. Foremost of these was the bitter strife among the various factions in the National Convention for control of the government. Finally the extremist Jacobins gained the upper hand, and called for the arrest and execution of Louis XVI as a traitor to France. They had evidence, they claimed, that he was "guilty of conspiracy against public liberty and of attacks upon the general security." Louis was tried late in December of 1792 and sent to the guillotine on January 21, 1793.

Hardly had word of the king's execution become known outside the borders of France than first England, and then Spain, declared war on the Republic. Now most of Europe was in arms against France in order to preserve the whole institution of monarchy. Fear for its very existence gripped France and its representative government. To prevent disorganization, the National Convention on March 25, 1793 appointed a Committee of Public Safety made up of Jacobins, gave it dictatorial powers, and thereby unleashed a reign of terror upon the people.

The Committee of Public Safety, headed by Danton, accepted nothing but total adherence to the government. Anyone suspected of the slightest difference of opinion could be accused of *incivisme*—disloyalty—and be sentenced by the Revolutionary Tribunal of the Committee to be guillotined. Never before, not even in the worst days of the monarchy, had men and women lived in such dread of being denounced, arrested, given a quick trial, and sent to the their deaths.

Tumbrels, the carts carrying the condemned to the guillotine, rumbled unceasingly over the cobblestones of Paris. True, many of those men and women were indeed enemies of the Republic, but many others were innocent victims of spite, hate, or jealousy. It became a mark of patriotism to whisper the word *incivisme* about someone, and so cause his arrest. As the tumbrels rolled through the streets, crowds gathered to watch, shouting invectives, clenching their fists, even throwing stones at the "citizens" being led to their executions.

Soon the Terrorists began to execute those of their own members who urged a cessation of the bloodshed. Maximilien Robespierre, seizing the reins, ordered Danton to the guillotine in July and intensified the search for "subversives". Now the revolution had gotten completely out of hand.

But what of Lavoisier in all this dreadful time? He was living at the Boulevard de la Madeleine, frantically trying to save the Academy, and also working on the two government committees to which he still belonged. Gone were all opportunities or even thoughts of scientific work; survival was uppermost in his mind. When, on August 8, 1793, a decree was issued closing the doors of the Academy altogether, he felt that the best part of his life had been closed with them.

The Terror gathered momentum as the months went by. Bloodthirsty cries of "to the guillotine" for all aristocrats

or suspected persons echoed through the streets of Paris
and in the halls of the Revolutionary Tribunal. Marie
Antoinette, so recently queen of France, was not spared.
She was accused of traitorous acts against the country and
sent to her execution in October. But Robespierre and his
supporters were still not satisfied. Still the tumbrels rumbled on to the Place de la Révolution where the guillotine
stood.

The affairs of one last, hated institution of the monarchy, that of the Farmers-General, as yet remained un-
settled. It was taking a longer time than had been expected
to straighten out the papers and books of the Tax-Farm.
Inflamed by extremists impatient to settle its accounts, the
National Convention therefore, on November 24, 1793,
ordered the arrest of all of the Farmers-General.

On learning that a warrant for his arrest had been issued,
Lavoisier became panic-stricken. He feared not so much
for his person as for the inability to continue his work that
imprisonment would cause. Before he could be taken into
custody he went into hiding in the old rooms of the Academy. From there, he wrote a letter to the National Convention asking that the order for his arrest be reconsidered.
The letter reminded the members that he had taken no
part in the work of the Farmers-General for three years
and that in fact until recently he had been Commissioner
of the National Treasury. He added that his main interest
was science and as National Commissioner of Weights
and Measures he had carried out his duties with zeal and
success.

The letter was not even given the respect of being read
before the Convention. Instead, it was passed on to the
Committee of Public Instruction. Not a voice was raised

in Lavoisier's favor, although many of the committee members knew of the scientist's valuable work. Lavoisier, then, fearing for the life of his father-in-law Jacques Paulze, who had been arrested with the other Farmers-General, gave himself up on November 28th. He was taken to the Porte-Libre prison to a cell already occupied by his father-in-law and one other prisoner.

Here, in prison, the Farmers-General were expected to finish the accounts of the Tax Farm. The prisoners were cheerful, confident they would be released as soon as their work was done. At the worst, they felt, their property would be confiscated. Lavoisier considered his own position better than most of the others because, he said, he could always make a living as a pharmacist.

Prison life was not as grim as Lavoisier had thought it would be. The cell was not too cramped; it even had a fireplace to furnish heat, and there were no bars or bolts on the doors or windows. The only security measures taken were the placing of guards at the gates and the entrances to the corridors. Food and wine could be purchased and clothing and mail easily brought in. The prisoners were not confined to their cells, except for roll-call at nine o'clock at night. At all other times they could meet to discuss their common problems and to plan their defense.

Mme. Lavoisier, at first frantic with fear for the safety of both her father and her husband, soon got to work to seek their release. Tirelessly she visited officials, wrote letters, tried by every means she could think of to have the order for their arrest cancelled. All was in vain. On December 17, seals were placed on the doors of the house in the Boulevard de la Madeleine, and the estate at Freschines confiscated. Mme. Lavoisier was permitted to remain in the house but was not allowed to remove any of her husband's papers or apparatus from it.

A letter from Lavoisier to his wife showed how, despite his own troubles, he was most concerned about her welfare. It showed, too, that he was not so optimistic as he appeared to the other prisoners. He wrote: "You are worrying too much and exhausting yourself in body and spirit and I cannot share the burden. Take care that your health does not deteriorate for that would be the worst evil. My career is advanced and I have enjoyed a happy existence. As long as I can remember you have contributed to this and you continue to do so by the affection that you show me; eventually I shall leave behind me recollections of appreciation and devotion. Thus my task is accomplished, but you, who have a right to expect a long life ahead of you should not throw it away. Yesterday I thought you appeared sad; but why should this be so when I am completely resigned to everything and will consider as gained everything that I do not lose. Besides, we still have some chance of being together again and in the meantime your visits give me some happy moments."

A few days after his house was sealed by order of the Convention, Lavoisier was brought to it under guard to watch Fourcroy and de Morveau remove papers and materials belonging to the Committee on Weights and Measures. We do not know whether any word was exchanged between Lavoisier and the two men he had helped establish in their scientific careers. Nor do we know what thoughts passed through his mind, knowing his two collaborators on the *Nomenclature de Chimique* and *Annales de Chimie* were doing nothing on his behalf. Were they jealous of his reputation as a great chemist or of his former wealth when they had been poor? When Lavoisier was returned to the prison, his thoughts must have been bitter indeed.

The Farmers-General were finding it impossible to complete the task of rendering the accounts of the Tax-Farm as long as they remained in the Porte-Libre prison, with no access to many of their records. Upon application, they were transferred on Christmas Eve of 1793 to the offices of the Farmers-General where, with windows and doors barred, they got to work with a will. By the end of January they had finished, the records and accounts were in order, and they expected to be released.

But they had not reckoned with the blood-thirsty Reign of Terror. Suddenly, to their dismay, new accusations were hurled against them. One was the charge that they had been remiss in their payments to the State and had lent out money at excessive rates of interest. Another, and more serious one in the eyes of the Convention, was that the tobacco they had sold had been adulterated with water and other ingredients harmful to the health of the people. The Farmers-General remained imprisoned in their offices while the Convention and its committees debated the charges.

Lavoisier, in common with the others, now began to grasp the extreme seriousness of their situation. The Revolutionary Tribunal was sending people indiscriminately to the guillotine for no other offense than having once held office in the monarchy. Anyone of noble birth or in any way connected with an *émigré* or who could not show a certificate of loyalty was liable to execution. Even past membership in the long-disbanded "Club de 1789" had become a crime. Suspects were brought before the

Tribunal, given a trial of sorts lasting a few minutes, and condemned. No one was safe from the dictator Robespierre and his fanatical Jacobins. The Farmers-General were in mortal fear for their lives.

LAVOISIER IS TRIED AND EXECUTED

TWENTY-ONE

❧ ANOTHER THREE MONTHS dragged by as the fate of the Farmers-General hung in the balance. Lavoisier used this time to begin preparing his defense against what were to him obviously false charges. As one measure, he asked the Bureau of Consultation of Arts and Crafts for a certificate of his services to the state. The certificate, sent to Lavoisier and recorded in the records as well, acknowledged his great work as a distinguished chemist who had brought honor to France. Others sent letters he could use attesting to the importance of his work and his loyalty. One friend even tried vainly to have his case separated from the other Farmers-General, hoping thus to have him acquitted.

But the greatest disappointment Lavoisier bore was the silence of his friends in powerful governmental positions. Neither did any of the scientists in the National Convention raise their voices in protest against his arrest. Perhaps they were afraid to come to his aid lest they, too, be accused of disloyalty, for during those terrible days few dared take up the cause of an accused. Only Mme. Lavoisier, with the lives of the two she loved most at stake, feared nothing in trying to gather evidence for their defense.

Then, on the afternoon of May 5, 1794, the blow fell. The National Convention issued a decree calling for the Farmers-General to be brought to trial before the Revolutionary Tribunal.

The first to learn of this was Lavoisier, who hurried off to tell the others the terrifying news. Now none of those imprisoned in the offices could pretend to be optimistic any longer. True, they would be given a trial, but they knew it would be a mockery of justice. Barring a miracle, their doom was sealed, for few indeed were ever acquitted by the Tribunal.

Hurriedly, they took counsel among themselves. Personal papers were hastily burned, farewell letters written, despair took over. Some of the Farmers-General had hidden opium with which to take their own lives should such a catastrophe happen, but Lavoisier dissuaded them from doing so. He said to them, "Why go to meet death? Because it is dishonorable to receive it by the decree of another, especially by an unjust decree? For us, the very outrageousness of the injustice wipes out the dishonor. . . . To take our own lives would be to acquit the madmen who are sending us to death. Let us think of those who have preceded us to the scaffold and at all events leave a good example to those who will follow."

In the evening, the Farmers-General were herded into covered wagons and taken to the Concièrgerie prison.

There, miserable, cold, and hungry, they huddled together knowing the same fate awaited all of them. Lavoisier gave what comfort he could to his old father-in-law Paulze, yet could find no comfort within himself. There is no record of any farewell letter he may have written to his beloved wife, but the letter to his cousin Augez de Villers is heart-breaking. Lavoisier wrote:

"I have had a fairly long life, above all a very happy one, and I think that I shall be remembered with some regrets and perhaps leave some reputation behind me. What more could I ask? The events in which I am in-volved will probably save me from the troubles of old age. I shall die in full possession of my faculties, and that is another advantage that I should count among those that I have enjoyed. If I have any distressing thoughts, it is of not having done more for my family; to be unable to give either to them or to you any token of my affection and my gratitude is to be poor indeed.

"So it is true that the practice of every social virtue, im-portant services for one's country, a life spent advan-tageously in the advancement of the useful arts and of human knowledge are not enough to protect a man from a sinister end or to avoid dying like a criminal!

"I am writing to you today, because tomorrow perhaps I may no longer be allowed to do so, and because it is a comfort to me in these last moments to think of you and of those who are dear to me. Do not forget that this letter is for all those who are concerned about me. It is probably the last that I shall write to you."

Early in the morning of May 8, the accused were per-mitted to consult for fifteen minutes with the four lawyers appointed to defend all the thirty-one of them. The prisoners were then searched and their valuables removed as though they were already being prepared for execution. Then they were told to follow a police officer, who led them down a dark corridor and through a low door into the Palais de Justice, and into the courtroom.

Ironically, the courtroom was called the Salle de la Liberté—the Liberty Room. There on a dais sat three judges in black silk coats with the tricolor band of the Republic slantwise across their chests, their three-plumed black caps of office on their heads. To the side sat the jury. The closely-guarded prisoners were seated on a series of steps facing their judges.

The prosecutor rose to attack the Farmers-General in violent terms. "The record of the crimes of these vampires is complete; their crimes clamor for vengeance; the immorality of these creatures is burned into public memory; they are the cause of all the evils that have for some time afflicted France."

Then the lawyers for the defense were given a very brief opportunity to answer. To the plea that Lavoisier's work was of immeasurable importance to France, and to the certificate of the Bureau of Consultation, there was no reply on the part of the judges. They were brushed aside as of no consequence. The judges had made up their minds before the trial that the defendants were guilty. The unanimous decision of the jury was "guilty." Outside, in the courtyard, the tumbrels were already waiting to take the victims to the guillotine, for none doubted the outcome of the farcical trial.

It was four o'clock on the warm, still afternoon of May 8, 1794 when the prisoners were taken from the courtroom to be driven to their deaths. Few crowds watched as

Lavoisier's death certificate. (From the Denis I. Duveen Collection)

the tumbrels carrying them rode through the streets, few shouts of anger and insult rose against the condemned. The people of Paris had grown tired of the incessant blood-letting and were beginning to pity those who were about to die.

For the last time, Lavoisier crossed the Seine and rode past the buildings and gardens familiar to him all of his fifty years. What were his thoughts? Did he forgive the people of France, feeling they too were in a sense victims of the Terror? We shall never know, for he rode silently to his death.

"It took only a moment to make this head fall, and a hundred years will perhaps not be enough to produce another like it." With these words, the scientist Joseph-Louis Lagrange, a day after Lavoisier's execution, spoke a fitting epitaph for Antoine-Laurent Lavoisier.

AFTER LAVOISIER'S DEATH

MARIE PAULZE LAVOISIER, having lost both husband and father within a few minutes, was ordered arrested on June 14. But the Terror had run its course with the execution in July of Robespierre himself, the worst Terrorist of all, and in August Mme. Lavoisier was released. Penniless, she was given shelter by an old servant who took care of her until March, 1795. Then a decree was passed returning the personal property of the Farmers-General to their widows and children. The decree called them the unjustly condemned Farmers-General," an admission ten months too late to save their lives. Marie returned to her home, there to work on the completion of the memoirs her late husband had begun before his death. In time she again invited scientists and artists to her home, but those who had done nothing to help save her husband never crossed her threshold.

A few years after Lavoisier's death, his friend Pierre Samuel duPont de Nemours emigrated to America with his two sons and their families. The younger son, Éleuthère Irénée, trained in Lavoisier's laboratory, set up a gunpowder plant in Delaware which he first called the "Lavoisier Mill." The name was later changed to E. I. duPont de Nemours and Company, and has since become famous throughout the world wherever chemical products are sold.

Nor did Joseph Priestley remain untouched by the French Revolution. As early as 1789 he had shown great sympathy for the French in their struggle for freedom. Because of this, in 1791 on the July anniversary of the fall of the Bastille, his house in Birmingham was burned by a drunken mob. Priestley fled to London, but continued to be persecuted, especially when the National Assembly conferred French citizenship upon him. At last, in April, 1794, he set sail for America to make a new home for himself and his family. He arrived in New York in June, a month after Lavoisier's execution, and settled in Northumberland, Pennsylvania. There his home still stands as a museum and memorial to the discoverer of oxygen.

As for the people of France, the blood-bath of the Reign of Terror taught them a valuable lesson. Suddenly, they woke to the true meaning of the cry of the revolution: "Liberty, Equality, Fraternity." Order rose out of chaos and gave birth to a true democracy, the great Republic of France. In time, the Academy of Science was re-opened, and remains the most important scientific body in France.

Lavoisier's work has remained the cornerstone of modern chemistry. Beginning with his questioning of the phlogiston theory in 1772, he brought chemistry from the last outposts of the alchemists to its position as a modern science. He rang the death knell of the phlogiston theory, showed the true nature of combustion, and helped give chemistry a new nomenclature. Above all, the clear logic of his scientific thinking set an example to chemists everywhere of how one must approach a problem scientifically.

France lost much during the revolution and the Terror, but perhaps its greatest loss was that of Antoine-Laurent Lavoisier. For the increase he brought to man's sum of knowledge the world will never forget him.

IMPORTANT DATES IN THE
LIFE OF LAVOISIER

1743—August 26—Born in Paris.
1748—Death of mother, goes to live with grandmother
and aunt.
1754—Enrolled as day student at Collège Mazarin.
1761—Enters School of Law.
1763—Works with Guettard on geological atlas of
France.
Graduates from School of Law.
1765—First paper presented before Academy of Science,
on plaster of Paris.
1766—Receives medal from King for essay on street lighting.
1767—Travels with Guettard to study geology of France.
Final abandonment of law profession.

1768—Buys into the Farmers-General.

Elected to Academy of Science as "adjoint" or junior member.

1769—Completes experiment to show water does not turn into soil.

1771—Marries Marie Anne Pierrette Paulze.

1772—Experiments with diamonds.

Lavoisier first begins to question the phlogiston theory.

Experiments with calcination of metals.

Experiments with combustion of sulphur and phosphorus.

Sealed note regarding gain in weight of metals in calcination and sulphur and phosphorus in burning, deposited at Academy.

1773—Laboratory memorandum regarding experiments to be done on burning.

1774—January—Publication of *Opuscules Physiques et Chimiques.*

1774—Meets Joseph Priestley in Paris.

1775—Presents paper before Academy on discovery of "eminently respirable air" which had the ability to calcine metals and to make flames burn more brightly.

1775—Becomes Gunpowder Commissioner and moves to Arsenal. Sets up laboratory at Arsenal.

1775—Death of father.

1776—Arrival of Benjamin Franklin in Paris and meeting with Lavoisier.

1777—Reads many papers before Academy attacking the phlogiston theory.

1778—Buys experimental farm at Freschines.

1779—Lavoisier renames "eminently respirable air" oxygen.

1780—Lavoisier submits report on prisons to Academy.

1781—Death of Mlle. Constance Punctis.

1782—Experiments on respiration with Pierre Simon Laplace.

Use of ice calorimeter.

1783—Publication of *Réflexions sur Phlogistique*.

Montgolfier Brothers' balloon experiments and Lavoisier's report concerning them. Suggests use of "inflammable air" to fill balloons.

Report of composition of water read before the Academy. No mention of work of Cavendish in this area.

Controversy over priority of discovery of composition of water.

1784—Report on mesmerism submitted.

Lavoisier decomposes water as further proof of its composition.

1785—Large-scale decomposition and synthesis of water.

Conversion of many chemists to anti-phlogiston theory.

Hospital report submitted to Academy.

1787—Publication of *Méthode de Nomenclature Chimique*.

Meeting of Assembly at Orléans. Lavoisier takes active part in its proceedings.

1788—Portrait of Franklin by Mme. Lavoisier sent to Philadelphia.

1789—Publication of *Traité Élémentaire de Chimie*.

Founding of new chemical publication, *Annales de Chimie*.

Further experiments on respiration, with Armand Séguin.

Meeting of States-General in Versailles to solve financial crisis in French government. Third Estate captures control of States-General.

Storming of the Bastille—outbreak of the French Revolution.

1790—Appointed to Commission on Weights and Measures.

Lavoisier's study of the economic wealth of France published as *Territorial Wealth of France*.

1791—Tax-Farm annulled. Lavoisier officially severs connection with it.

Lavoisier becomes Commissioner for the Royal Treasury.

New moderate constitutional monarchy set up by National Assembly.

1792—Lavoisier resigns as Commissioner of National Treasury.

1792—Austria and Prussia declare war on France.

King suspended from office.

Jacobins gain control of the National Assembly, call for a National Convention.

Lavoisier resigns from Gunpowder Commission and moves from Arsenal.

Monarchy officially abolished, France becomes a republic.

1793—Louis XVI executed as traitor to France.

England and Spain declare war on France.

Committee of Public Safety set up by National Convention.

Reign of Terror in France, with Danton and Robespierre at the head.

Academy of Science disbanded by decree of Convention.

Marie Antoinette executed.

Lavoisier arrested with other Farmers-General to complete report on their finances.

1794—May 8—Lavoisier and other Farmers-General tried before Revolutionary Tribunal, and executed.

INDEX